D1293771

SONGS
THAT
CHANGED
THE WORLD

SONGS
THAT
CHANGED
THE WORLD

Edited by

Wanda Willson Whitman

CROWN PUBLISHERS, INC., NEW YORK

ACKNOWLEDGMENTS

Special gratitude is due Sis Cunningham and Gordon Friesen of *Broadside* magazine, and to Irwin Silber of *Sing Out!* for advice and counsel; and also to Sis Cunningham for her transcriptions of songs first appearing in *Broadside*. Aletha Robinson rates special notice for her editing of music arrangements.

Book publishers granting permission to reprint include Harcourt, Brace & World, Inc., for songs from Carl Sandburg's *Songbag:* "Three Grains of Corn," "Boll Weevil Song," "La Cucaracha," "Drill, Ye Tarriers, Drill," "John Henry," and "It's the Syme the Whole World Over;" and also The Macmillan Company for "Sweet Betsy from Pike" from *Songs of the Great American West,* Silber and Robinson, and "Jana Gana Mana" from Rabindrinath Tagore's book of poems, *Gitanjali.*

The Music Project of the Works Progress Administration (WPA) found "I Am a Little Christian" in Appalachia. Leo Feist, Inc., granted permission for George F. Cohan's "Over There," as did Edward B. Marks Music Corporation for "Strange Fruit." Songwriters, composers, and translators Harold Rome, Earl Robinson, Jay Gormey, Phil Ochs, Malvina Reynolds, Pete Seeger, and Eric Bentley also were helpful, as were the staffs of the music research library in Lincoln Center, New York, and the copyright office of the Library of Congress.

Second Printing, May, 1970

© 1969 by Wanda Willson Whitman
Library of Congress Catalog Card Number: 73–75061
Manufactured in the United States of America
Published simultaneously in Canada by
General Publishing Company Limited

PREFACE

"Let who will make the laws of a nation if I may make its songs" is a saying often attributed to Heine, although anthologies provide an earlier version from a seventeenth-century English writer, Andrew Fletcher of Saltoun: "Give me the making of the songs of a nation and I care not who makes its laws." *

Whatever its source—perhaps, like a folk song, the product of various minds—the saying has meaning today. In an era of crises and transition, young Americans have burst into song, made their own verses to new or familiar tunes strummed on guitars, and carried their criticisms of society around the world to blend with drumbeats, the sound of sitars, and singing voices from other lands. Whether or not musical protest proves effective today, its long-term social action has been a factor in history, from "The World Turned Upside Down," played at the Yorktown surrender, to "Go Down, Moses," in Mississippi.

Whether a song only reflects or truly activates a given change has been a factor in choosing the songs published here, but is not always easy to determine. Certain songs inspire an emotional response that rouses and channels public opinion and eventually affects public action. The popular lyric can betray prejudice or spread enlightenment, and the process can continue over a long period, as in the case of time-honored religious or patriotic songs. Among songs of our own times, one may argue whether "Blowin' in the Wind" or "We Shall Overcome" has done more for the civil rights movement in the United States, but obviously both have contributed; "Blowin' in the Wind" on jukeboxes and radio reached the white readers of *Gone With the Wind,* while "We Shall Overcome" gave courage to Negro marchers on the long road to Freedom Now, and is still sung around the world by hopeful dissenters in other causes.

Many minds have contributed to this collection, as well as sources from Washington to Jerusalem. Thanks are long overdue to helpful librarians, song collectors, and friends.

WANDA WILLSON WHITMAN

New York, North Carolina, and Texas
1969

* *Convention Concerning a Right Regulation of Government for the Common Good of Mankind,* 1703.

CONTENTS

I

SONGS OF REVOLUTION

Today many people believe that the world progresses by revolution, turning over and over again in movement toward the human hope that all men are created equal and endowed by their Creator with certain inalienable rights. The first specific and effective challenge to established political authority, property rights, and accustomed order was of course the revolution of the American colonies. The songs that best expressed the material causes and the lasting effects of that revolution were, at the beginning, "Revolutionary Tea" and, at the end, "The World Turned Upside Down"—the one showing the apparently trivial economic occasion for rebellion, and the other, the surprising and enduring effects of revolutionary victory. Following the United States, the French Revolution's "Ça Ira" provided a musical accompaniment to fighting at the barricades and storming the Bastille. ("The Marseillaise," though commonly credited with revolutionary origin and certainly án inspiration to later revolts, was a war song originating in the army during the war with Burgundy.)

Around the world, revolutionary movements brought the breath of freedom and accompanying struggles to both hemispheres. For decades the Irish sang of a hoped-for freedom which, with that of other small nations of Europe, was to come as a welcome by-product of World War I. At almost the same time, Latin America gained by the Mexican Revolution, with its down-to-earth marching song "La Cucaracha." Although national aspirations motivated the revolutionary movements at their beginning, the world aspect of change would be expressed in the "Internationale," still so foreign to American thought that its brief introduction in a Federal Theatre play (Class of '29, to convey the despair of jobless students) would count against the project in congressional debate. In Europe and Asia the song fared better; Spanish Republicans sang it with their anti-Fascist allies in the civil war, who brought with them from Germany their own shout for freedom. In Asia, along with "The East Is Red," the international idea spread, as did rebellion, from Peking to China's neighbors.

Today in America, although the great changes of our time have come with song in the crusades for civil rights and equal opportunities, a sense of the menace of modern war has changed the emphasis. As of now, the revolutionary dissent in this country stresses not armed revolt but the urgent need, in the atomic age, for permanent peace.

1

REVOLUTIONARY TEA

All versions of this song agree that the world's most famous tempest in a teapot was caused by "taxation without representation." It is also clear that in 1776 there was a "generation gap" between Mother England and the young, impatient colonists declaring their independence.

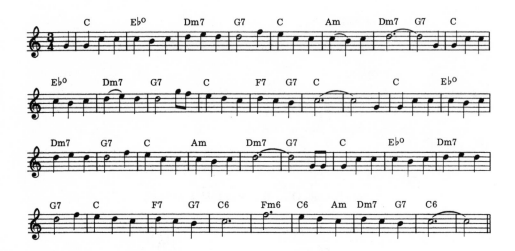

There was an old lady lived over the sea,
And she was an island queen;
Her daughter lived off in a new countrie,
With an ocean of water between.
The old lady's pockets were filled with gold,
But never contented was she,
So she called on her daughter to pay her a tax,
Of three pence a pound on the tea,
Of three pence a pound on the tea.

"Now mother, dear mother," the daughter
        replied,
"I shan't do the thing you ax;
I'm willing to pay a fair price for the tea,
But never the three penny tax."
"You shall," quoth the mother, and reddened
        with rage,
"For you're my own daughter, you see,
And sure 'tis quite proper the daughter should
        pay,
Her mother a tax on the tea,
Her mother a tax on the tea."

And so the old lady her servant called up,
And packed off a budget of tea,
And eager for three pence a pound, she put in
Enough for a large familie.
She ordered her servant to bring home the tax,
Declaring her child should obey,
Or old as she was and a woman most grown,
She'd half whip her life away,
She'd half whip her life away.

The tea was conveyed to the daughter's door,
And all down by the ocean side,
And the bouncing girl poured out every pound,
In the dark and boiling tide,
And then she called out to the island queen,
"O mother, dear mother," quoth she,
"Your tea you may have when 'tis steeped
        enough,
But never a tax from me,
But never a tax from me."

THE LIBERTY SONG

Belonging also to the revolutionary period, since the last verse offers a token loyalty to Britain, this song was still sung during the War of 1812. The music was composed for David Garrick; the lyric reads like a modern political platform—and note the appeal for funds. Brown University Collection.

Come join hand in hand, brave Americans call,
And rouse your bold hearts at fair Liberty's call.
No tyrannous acts shall suppress your just claim,
Or stain with dishonor America's name.

Chorus:
In Freedom we're born and in Freedom we'll live,
Our purses are ready—steady, Friends, steady—
Not as slaves but as freemen our money we'll give.

Our worthy forefathers—let's give them a cheer,
To climates unknown did courageously steer;
Through oceans, to deserts, for freedom they came
And dying bequeathed us their freedom and fame.—*Cho.*

Their generous bosoms all dangers despised,
So highly, so wisely, their birthright they prized.
We'll keep what they gave, we will piously keep,
Nor frustrate their toils on the land and the deep.—*Cho.*

The Tree their own hands had to liberty reared
They lived to behold growing strong and revered;
With transport they cried, "Now our wishes we gain,
For our children shall gather the fruits of our pain."—*Cho.*

Swarms of placemen and pensioners soon will appear
Like locusts deforming the charms of the year.
Suns vainly will rise, showers vainly descend,
If we are to drudge for what others will spend.—*Cho.*

Then join hand in hand, brave Americans all,
By uniting we stand, by dividing we fall;
In so righteous a cause let us hope to succeed,
For Heaven approves of each generous deed.—*Cho.*

All ages shall speak with amaze and applause
Of the courage we'll show in support of our laws;
To die we can bear—but to serve we disdain,
For shame is to Freedom more dreadful than pain.—*Cho.*

This bumper I crown for our Sovereign's health,
And this for Britannia's glory and wealth;
That wealth and that glory immortal may be,
If she is but just—and if we are but free.—*Cho.*

THE WORLD TURNED UPSIDE DOWN

This is the song the English played at the surrender of Cornwallis. It seems now, prophetically, to identify loss of the American colonies with the unbelievable, apparently unimportant, first step in the long, slow dissolution of world empire. Tune and nursery rhyme are traditional.

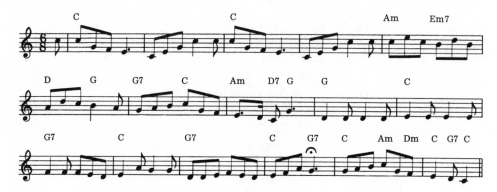

If buttercups buzzed after the bee,
If boats were on land, churches on sea,
If ponies rode men, and if grass ate the corn,
And cats should be chased into holes by the mouse,
If the mammas sold their babies to gypsies for half a crown,
If summer were spring, and the other way 'round,
Then all the world would be upside down.

LA CARMAGNOLE

After Lafayette took American ideas back to France, revolutionary French troops returned from Italy with a song for the revolution that, following the one in America, was more savage because it was a civil war. This song would be followed by another even more bloodthirsty. English translation by Jay Williams.

Madame Veto her promise gave,
Madame Veto her promise gave,
That all of France would be her slave,
That all of France would be her slave.
But she has paid the score,
Thanks to our cannon's roar!

Refrain:
Let's dance the Carmagnole, hail to the roar.
Let's dance the Carmagnole, thundering roar,
Hail to the roar.

Monsieur Veto he promised hard
His country faithfully to guard
His word he soon forgot—
We'll hang him on the spot.

Madam' Veto avait promis
De faire égorger tout Paris.
Mais son coup a manqué,
Grâce à nos cannoniers:

Refrain:
Dansons la Carmagnole,
Vive le son, Vive le son!
Dansons la Carmagnole,
Vive le son du canon.

ÇA IRA

Franklin is said to have been fond of the saying "Ça ira," meaning "This too will pass." The song, which became the official song of the Jacobins but was forbidden under the Directorate, conveys the fury of revolutionary threats put into action by a new weapon, the guillotine. Written in 1790 by M. Ladré, with music by De Bécourt; translation by Jay Williams.

Everything will go, it will go.
Hang the noble lords on every lamppost!
Yes, it will go, it will go, it will go.
All the noble lords in the streets
    shall swing!
Hang them and burn them and break
    their bones,
Down with 'em all from altars and thrones!
Yes, it will go, it will go, it will go,
Hang the noble lords on every lamppost—
Lords in the streets shall swing!

Ah! Ça ira, ça ira, ça ira,
Les aristocrats à la lanterne!
Ah! Ça ira, ça ira, ça ira,
Les aristocrats on les pendra!
Si'on n'les pend pas, on les romp'ra,
Si'on n'les romp pas, on les brûl'ra!

Ah! Ça ira, ça ira, ça ira,
Les aristocrats à la lanterne,
Ah! Ça ira, ça ira, ça ira,
Les aristocrats on les pendra!

RAKOCZI MARCH

When revolutionary winds swept Europe in the first half of the nineteenth century, a Hungarian bandmaster, Miklos Scholl, composed this famous march with its echoes of bugle calls and Gypsy music. Written in 1809, it was used as a musical theme for the revolutionary spirit by later composers, including Berlioz and Liszt.

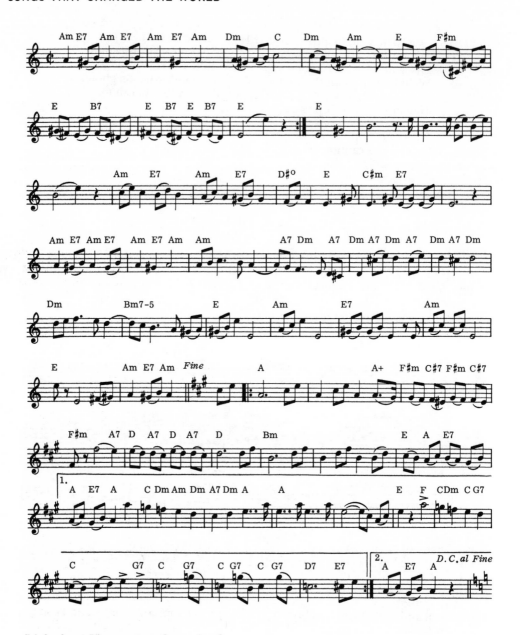

Light from Heaven guards our land,
Truth our shield in the field.
Light from heaven brightly guards our native homeland dear.
Red, white, green, these colors o'er you fly;
Sun of Magyar glory has not set.
Its rays still blaze high in our sky!
Men of proud Hungarian blood, if misfortune whelms you with its evil blows,
If dark the storm cloud grows,
Like a beacon, truth will guide you through darkest night,
Truth be your signal bright.
If the clouds gather quick, darken thick, and gloomy grows the sky,
Never let your courage die.
Heaven's arm will protect us from harm,
With Right endowed will pierce the cloud.
The proud Hungarian land will ne'er beneath a foeman's slave yoke bend.
Thou, Lord in Heaven, our dear land befriend.
We will our homes defend!

Űdv hazánkon égi fény!
Nemzet ore tiszta lény!
Űdv hazánkon égi fény!
O tiszta, tiszta lény!
Hármas a szivárványod,
A magyarnak azt jelentve,
Hogy nem tűnt, nem tűnt le napod:
Oh légy főlőtte napsugár!
A magyar, magyar ha tenger ár,
Habja minden csepp vizén
Rezgjen át a tiszta, tiszta fény,
Rezgyen át tiszta fény,
Rezgyen át a tiszta fény, tiszta, tiszta fény!

Hogy ha rád, hogy ha rád fátyolát
Fergeteg boritja el,
Fergeteg boritja el,
A sőtét, a sőtét melyőlét
Elem csatárna tépje fel.   Finis.
Ne veszszem a hon semmiségbe, semmiségbe,
Mi védjük itt, te védd, az égbe védd,
Te védd, as égbe védd.
Hogy ha rád. . . .

LA BRABANÇONNE

After the Netherlands, under William of Orange, gained freedom from Spanish rule, the usual divisions developed in the liberated area, and in 1830 this song declared the independence of Belgium from Dutch rule under the House of Orange. Note the "tree of liberty" symbol used in the American "Liberty Song."

Who would believe this arbitrary deed,
This hateful scheme of tyranny?
A friendly prince would on us speed,
With his bullets of wasteful lead.
'Tis finished now, ye Belgians brave!
We must Brabant from Nassau save!
Return the grapeshot which they gave.
The Orange may no longer wave,
The Orange may no longer wave
Upon the tree of liberty!
Upon the tree of liberty!

Men of Brabant, ye nation brave,
Who flinch not in the hottest fights!
With cannon-shot your country save,

And make Batavia grant your rights.
O'er Brussels, at St. Michael's feet,
Our banners proud for ever meet,
The haughty Orange to defeat
Under the tree of liberty!

Qui l'aurait dit de l'arbitraire,
Secondant les affreux projets,
Sur nous un prince sanguinaire,
Vient lancer des boulets,
C'en est fait, Belges, tout change,
Avec Nassau plus d'indignes traités,
La mitraille a brisé l'orange,
Sur l'arbre de la liberté.
Sur l'arbre de la liberté.

DIE GEDANKEN SIND FREI
(I Think As I Please)

German songs of revolutionary protest are among the oldest; this one goes back to the Peasant Wars of the sixteenth century. Sung again in a Schiller play revived during the Hitler era, it became popular once more until banned in the Third Reich. English translation by Arthur Kevess. Copyright 1950 by River Bend Music, Inc. All rights reserved. Used by permission.

I think as I please,
And this gives me pleasure,
My conscience decrees,
This right I must treasure;
My thoughts will not cater
To duke or dictator,
No man can deny—
Die Gedanken sind frei!

Ich denke was ich will,
Und was mich beglücket,
Doch alles in der Still,
Und wie es sich schicket.
Mein Wunsch und Begehren
Kann niemand verwehren,
Es bleibet dabei;
Die Gedanken sind frei!

And should tyrants take me
And throw me in prison,
My thoughts will burst free,
Like blossoms in season.
Foundations will crumble,
And structures will tumble,
And free men will cry—
Die Gedanken sind frei!

Und sperrt man mich ein
Im finsteren Kerker,
Das alles sind rein
Vergebliche Werke;
Denn meine Gedanken
Zerreissen die Schranken
Und Mauern entzwei:
Die Gedanken sind frei!

VÁLKA! VÁLKA!
(Czech War Song)

Bedrich Smetana, famous Czech composer, wrote the music in 1848, following the tradition of the Hussite battle songs. With words by J. J. Kolár, it was sung first in the 1848 rebellion against the Hapsburgs, and again during World War II.

Up, Czechs! War is here! Flags are flying!
Rouse ye men, on God relying.
Ne'er forget your nation's story—
Guard your homes and Czechish glory,
Guard your homes and Czechish glory!
Everywhere alarm bells toll,
Ancent Hussites' songs and soul.

Válka! Válka!
Prapor věje!
Vzhůru Češi,
Bůh nám přeje,
Stůjte pevně při svém právu,
Chraňte vlasť a Čechů slávu,
Chraňte vlasť a Čechů slávu!
Taký jest po vlasti hluk,
Táboritů zpěv a zvuk.

GARIBALDI'S HYMN
(Si Scopron Le Tombe . . .)

Sung by Garibaldi's troops in 1848, with the words by Mercantini set to music by A. Olivieri, this one lasted long enough to be suppressed by Mussolini in our own century.

The dark earth is gaping, in anguish is riven,
Arise! martyred heroes who for freedom have striven,
The sword and the wreath of the victor adorn you,
And Italy's name and her flame in your hearts.
For freedom and Italy! For freedom and Italy!
For Italy's freedom we'll drive out the foe.
Then forward, then forward, determined to conquer;
Then forward with Italy's flame in your hearts.
For freedom and Italy! For freedom and Italy!
For freedom and Italy we'll drive out the foe!

Thou land of song, overlong you've been sleeping,
Again from its scabbard your bright steel is leaping,
Our foemen surround us, their ranks we must sever,
Remember Legnano: be daring and bold!
The scourges of a foreign master never shall tame us,
Descendants of Rome, let the yoke never shame us;
Have patience no longer with German usurpers,

The day of our slavery's end now behold!
For freedom and Italy! For freedom and Italy!

For Italy's freedom we'll drive out the foe!
To battle! To battle!

Si scopron le tombe, si levano i morti,
I martiri nostri son tutti risorti;
Le spade nel pugno, gli allori alle chiome,
La fiamma ed il nome—d'Italia nel cor.
Sorgiamo! Sorgiamo! Su, o giovani schiere!
Su al vento per tutto le nostre bandiere!
Su tutti col ferro; su tutti col foco!
Su tutti col foco—d'Italia nel cor.

Va'fuori d'Italia, va'fuori, ch'è l'ora,
Va'fuori d'Italia, va'fuori, stranier!

LILLIBULLERO

This is one of the earliest of the many Irish songs of revolt. Richard Talbot was a new English governor of the rebel island, appointed by King James II. There are many verses, some in that ancient storehouse of poetry Percy's Reliques.

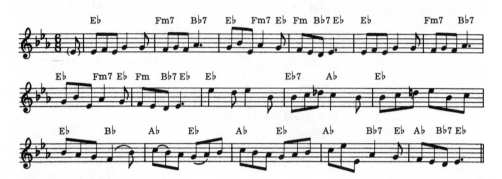

Ho! brother Teague, dost hear the decree,
Lillibullero, bullen-a-la,
That we shall have a new deputee?
Lillibullero, bullen-a-la.
Lero, lero, lillibullero,
    lillibullero, bullen-a-la,
Lero, lero, lillibullero,
    lillibullero, bullen-a-la.

For the good Talbot is made a lord,
Lillibullero, bullen-a-la,
And with brave lads is coming aboard.
Lillibullero, bullen-a-la.
Lero, lero, etc.

There was an old prophecy found in a bog,
Lillibullero, bullen-a-la,
"Ireland shall be ruled by an ass and a dog."
Lillibullero, bullen-a-la.
Lero, lero, etc.

And now this prophecy's come to pass,
Lillibullero, bullen-a-la,
For Talbot's the dog, and James is the ass.
Lillibullero, bullen-a-la.
Lero, lero, etc.

SEAN VAN VOGHT
(Poor Old Woman)

In this one, the French and the English, now under King William, are attacking each other, while the Irish are happy observers, much as the American colonists were when that war spread to American shores.

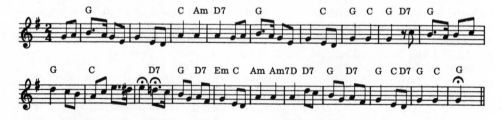

"Oh! the French are on the sea," says the Sean van Voght,
"Oh! the French are on the sea," says the Sean van Voght,
"The French are in the Bay, they'll be here at break of day,
And the Orange will decay," says the Sean van Voght,
"And the Orange will decay," says the Sean van Voght.

"And where will they have their camp?" says the Sean van Voght,
"And where will they have their camp?" says the Sean van Voght.

"On the Curragh of Kildare, and the boys will all be there
With their pikes in good repair," says the Sean van Voght,
"With their pikes in good repair," says the Sean van Voght.

"And what will the yeomen do?" says the Sean van Voght,
"And what will the yeomen do?" says the Sean van Voght,
"What will the yeomen do but throw off the red and blue,
And swear they will be true to the Sean van Voght?
And swear they will be true to the Sean van Voght?"

"Then what colour will be seen?" says the Sean van Voght,
"Then what colour will be seen?" says the Sean van Voght,
"What colour should be seen where our fathers' homes have been,
But our own immortal green?" says the Sean van Voght,
"But our own immortal green?" says the Sean van Voght.

"Will old Ireland then be free?" says the Sean van Voght,
"Will old Ireland then be free?" says the Sean van Voght.
"Old Ireland shall be free from the centre to the sea;
"Then hurrah for liberty," says the Sean van Voght,
"Then hurrah for liberty," says the Sean van Voght.

THE INTERNATIONALE

This most famous of all revolutionary songs has often in itself been the object of fear and hatred. Recently, Chinese Communist students were arrested for singing it at Stalin's tomb. There are no private claims to authorship.

Arise, you pris'ners of starvation! Arise, you wretched of the earth.
For justice thunders condemnation, a better world's in birth.
No more tradition's chain shall bind us,
Arise, you slaves, no more in thrall.
The earth shall rise on new foundations,
We have been naught, we shall be all.

Chorus:
'Tis the final conflict, let each stand in his place.
The Internationale shall be the human race!

LA CUCARACHA
(The Cockroach)

In Mexico's 1912–1916 revolution, a cockroach seemed the perfect symbol for the raids by Pancho Villa, whose followers disappeared into the night or the canyons south of the Border as the kitchen pest seems to vanish into thin air. Also appropriate, as the revolution spread, was the rapid proliferation of roaches. As for marijuana, that too would cross the Border in time.

All the maidens are of pure gold;
All the married girls are silver;
All the widows are of copper,
And old women merely tin.

Chorus:
The cucaracha, the cucaracha,
Doesn't want to travel on
Because she hasn't,
Oh, no, she hasn't,
Marijuana for to smoke.

All the girls up at Las Vegas
Are most awful tall and skinny,
But they're worse for plaintive pleading
Than the souls in Purgatory.—*Cho.*

All the girls here in the city
Don't know how to give you kisses,
While the ones from Albuquerque
Stretch their necks to avoid misses.

All the girls from Mexico
Are as pretty as a flower,
And they talk so very sweetly,
Fill your heart quite up with love.—*Cho.*

One thing makes me laugh most hearty—
Pancho Villa with no shirt on,
Now the Carranzistas beat it
Because Villa's men are coming.—*Cho.*

Las muchachas son de oro;
Las casadas son de plata;
Las viudas son de cobre,
Y las viejas oja de lata.

Chorus:
La cucaracha, la cucaracha,
Ya no quieres caminar,
Porque no tienes,
Porque le falta,
Marihuana que fumar.

Las muchachas de Las Vegas
Son muy altas y delgaditas,
Pero son mas pedigueñas
Que las animas benditas.—*Cho.*

Las muchachas de la villa
No saben ni dar un beso,
Cuando las de Albuquerque
Hasta estiran el pescuezo.—*Cho.*

Las muchachas Mexicanas
Son lindas como una flor,
Y hablan tan dulcemente
Que encantan de amor.—*Cho.*

Una cosa me da risa—
Pancho Villa sin camisa.
Ya se van los Carranzistas
Porque vienen los Villistas.—*Cho.*

CHI LAI
(Rise Up)

Translated by Tien-Han for a musical arrangement by Lee Pao-Ch'en, this song of China's revolution was also sung by soldiers in World War II. Like so many revolutionary songs, it urges "March on! March on!"

Arise, ye who refuse to be bondslaves!
With our very flesh and blood let us build
    our new Great Wall.
China's masses have met the day of danger,
Hate and anger fill the heart of all our
    countrymen.

Arise! Arise! Arise!
Many hearts with one mind
Brave the enemy's gunfire.
March on!
Brave the enemy's gunfire—
March on! March on! March on! On!

THE EAST IS RED

Sweeping from Shansi Province over the mainland, and sung in all countries friendly to the China of today, this song has perhaps the widest circulation of any modern revolutionary song. Arrangement by Ho Lu-Ting.

From the Red East rises the sun.
There appears in China Mao Tse-tung.
He works for the people's welfare.
He is the people's great savior.

Chairman Mao loves the people.
He is our guide.
He leads us onward
To build up New China.

QUÉ LINDA ES CUBA!
(How Lovely Is Cuba!)

This popular song from the Cuban revolution expresses a defensive love of the land, with a fidelity to Fidel associated with life in the cane fields. Lyrics and music by Eduardo Saborit.

Listen, you who say our country is less
    beautiful,
Listen, you who say our country is less good!
I ask you to look the whole world over for a
    sky that's as blue as the sky over you;
Or a moonlight as bright as the light of our
    moon
As it shines through the sweetness of cane.
Or a Fidel whose step shakes the mountains,
Or a flag to compare with our star.

Chorus:
How lovely, how lovely is Cuba—
Who defends her must love her the best!
Fair is her sky, fair is her sea,
She'll be a fortress of liberty—
Every good Cuban knows this well,
Faithful to death beside Fidel.

Oye: tú que dices que tu patria no es tan
    linda;
Oye: tú que dices que lo tuyo no es tan bueno;
Yo invito a que busque por el mundo
Otro cielo tan azul como tu cielo.
Una luna tan brillante como áquella
Que se filtre la dulcura da la caña.
Un Fidel que vibra en las montañas,
Un rubie, cinco franjas, y una estrella!

Chorus:
Cuba, qué linda es Cuba! *(Repeat.)*
Quien la defiende, la quiere más! *(Repeat.)*
Bello es tu cielo, bello es tu mar,
Eres un faro de libertad!

GO DOWN, MOSES

Negro spirituals trace back to the Old Testament, and of them all, Moses' mission to "Let my people go" has one of the strongest appeals today. This and the other Negro songs go back and forth in time for all people.

When Israel was in Egypt's land,
Let my people go!
Oppressed so hard they could not stand,
Let my people go!
Go down, Moses, way down in Egypt's land,
Tell old Pharaoh, Let my people go!

When Israel stood by the water side,
Let my people go!
At the command of God it did divide,
Let my people go!
Go down, Moses, way down in Egypt's land,
Tell old Pharaoh, Let my people go!

JOSHUA FIT THE BATTLE OF JERICHO

Here is an early spiritual that would carry to triumph the faith and fortitude of American Negroes, whose long and patient endurance found in Judeo-Christian teaching an aid to peaceful progress and accomplishment.

Joshua fit the battle of Jericho,
    Jericho, Jericho,
Joshua fit the battle of Jericho,
And the walls came tumbling down.

You may talk about your kings of Gideon,
You may talk about your men of Saul.
But there's none like good old Joshua
At the battle of Jericho.

Right up to the walls of Jericho
He marched with a spear in his hand.
"Go blow that ram's horn," Joshua cried,
" 'Cause the battle am in my hand."

Then the lamb, ram, sheep-horns began to
    blow,
And the trumpets began to sound,
Joshua commanded the children to shout,
And the walls came tumbling down.

I'M ON MY WAY

"He travels the fastest who travels alone"—the pioneer in any movement needs the courage to go ahead. When others say "no," this spiritual says "now."

I'm on my way (I'm on my way) and I won't
    turn back; *(Repeat twice.)*
I'm on my way, great God, I'm on my way.
I asked my brother to come with me. . . .
If he says no, I'll go alone.

I asked my sister to come with me.
If she says no, I'll go alone.
I asked my boss to let me go,
If he says no, I'll go anyhow.
I'm on my way to Freedom land.

WITH MY MIND STAYED ON FREEDOM

This song of the civil-rights marchers emphasizes the determination needed to sing in the streets, prepared to spend a night in jail, and wake up in the morning ready for more of the same. A SNCC song sung in the South in the early 60's. Used by permission.

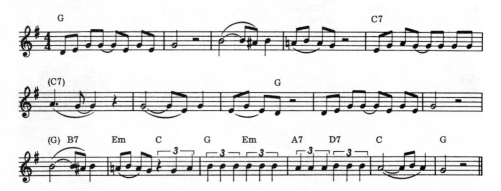

Woke up this morning with my mind stayed on freedom (oh, well I)
Woke up this morning with my mind stayed on freedom (oh, well I)
Woke up this morning with my mind (my mind it was) stayed on freedom,
Hallelu, hallelu, hallelu, hallelu, hallelujah!

Ain't no harm to keep your mind stayed on freedom,
Ain't no harm to keep your mind stayed on freedom,
Ain't no harm to keep your mind stayed on freedom,
Hallelu, hallelu, hallelu, hallelu, hallelujah!

Walkin' and talkin' with my mind stayed on freedom . . .
Singing' and prayin' with my mind stayed on freedom . . .
Doin' the twist with my mind stayed on freedom . . .

OH, FREEDOM

After a hundred years of promised emancipation, this song is still sung in the South. Indeed, long after the Civil War but long before today's freedom movement, it was sung by courageous black citizens of Atlanta, moving through the city in one of the earliest peaceful parades.

Oh, freedom, freedom! Oh, freedom, freedom!
Oh, freedom over me!
And before I'd be a slave, I'll be buried
    in my grave
And go home to my Lord and be free.

No more Jim Crow ...
No more moaning ...
No more weeping ...
There'll be singing ...

WE SHALL OVERCOME

Most celebrated of today's freedom songs, this one began at Highlander Folk School in the Tennessee mountains, with the adaptation of a union song that had in turn been derived from a hymn. New words and music arranged by Zilphia Horton, Frank Hamilton, Guy Carawan and Pete Seeger, with TRO copyright 1960 and 1965 by Ludlow Music, Inc., New York. All rights reserved. Used by permission.

We will overcome, we will overcome,
We will overcome some day.
Oh, deep in my heart, I do believe
We'll overcome some day.

First Line changes:

We will all be free, we will all be free ...

Black and white together ...

We will live in peace ...

We will end Jim Crow ...

The Lord will see us through.

II

SONGS OF PATRIOTISM

Between "My country, 'tis of thee, sweet land of liberty," and "My country, right or wrong!" an ethical gap is now perceived. But as a child wants to believe "My father can lick your father!" a young nation may need enthusiastic belief in its heritage, and songs of defense or self-justification may belong to one stage of growth. Both *The Marseillaise* and *The Watch on the Rhine* began as songs of defense, and the former, first sung against Burgundy, was repeated against the same foe in 1914 when a correspondent, describing mobilization for World War I, wrote: "Ten thousand Frenchmen filled the street. . . . They sang the 'Marseillaise' for two hours," and concluded, "A nation with a song and a patriotism such as I had witnessed could not . . . again be vanquished."

Small countries fighting for years or even centuries to gain their independence have produced some of the most enduring songs, exemplified by the Scottish ballads and the nostalgic songs of Irish exiles. But love of country, apart from struggle, makes for moving songs in countries large or small, with a range from "America the Beautiful" to "Meadowlands," and from "Killarney" to "The Road to Eilat."

BONNIE DUNDEE

Often attributed to Sir Walter Scott, this ballad had an earlier origin, but Scott may well have contributed an improved version. The tune is traditional.

To the Lairds of Convention 'twas Claverhouse spoke,
"Ere the King's crown go down there are crowns to be broke;
Then let each Cavalier who loves honor and me,
Come follow the bonnets of Bonnie Dundee."

Come fill up my cup, come fill up my can,
Saddle my horses and call out my men,
Then it's open the West Port and let us gae free,
And it's follow the bonnets of Bonnie Dundee.

Dundee he is mounted, he rides up the street,
The bells they ring backward, the drums they are beat,

But the Provost, douce man, says, "Just e'en let him be,
For the town is well rid of that de'il of Dundee."

There are hills beyond Pentland, and lands beyond Forth,
Be there lairds in the South, there are chiefs in the North,
There are brave Duniewassals, three thousand times three,
Will cry "Hai!" for the bonnets of Bonnie Dundee.

Then awa' to the hills, to the leas, to the rocks,
Ere I own a usurper, I'll couch with the fox,
Then tremble, false Whigs, in the midst of your glee,
Ye hae no seen the last of my bonnets and me!

THE CAMPBELLS ARE COMIN'

Scottish clan calls have echoed down the centuries with an emotional appeal not yet lost, and the Campbell clan had one of the most stirring. Words and tune are traditional.

The Campbells are comin', O ho, O ho. The Campbells are comin', O ho, O ho!
The Campbells are comin' to bonnie Lochleven, the Campbells are coming,
    O ho! O ho!
Up on the Lomonds I lay, I lay, up on the Lomonds I lay, I lay.
I looked down to bonnie Lochleven and heard three bonnie pipers play.
The Campbells are comin', etc.

The great Argyle, he goes before. He makes his cannon loudly roar;
Wi' sound of trumpet, pipe, and drum, the Campbells are comin', etc.

The Campbells they are a' in arms, their loyal faith and truth to show.
With banners rattlin' in the wind, the Campbells are comin', etc.

THE WEARING OF THE GREEN

This plaintive song traveled around the world with the Irish exiles after the rebellion of 1798. At home in Dublin it would in time supply a title, The Rising of the Moon, *for Lady Gregory's play. Meanwhile O. Henry's story gave Americans a parody: "They're killing men and women for the lacking of the green."*

O, Paddy dear, and did you hear the news that's going 'round?
The shamrock is forbid by law to grow on Irish ground.
St. Patrick's day no more we'll keep, his colours can't be seen,
For there's a cruel law against the wearing of the green.

I met with Napper Tandy, and he took me by the hand,
And he said, "How's poor old Ireland, and how does she stand?
She's the most distressful country that ever yet was seen,
They're hanging men and women for the wearing of the green."

Then since the colour we must wear is England's cruel red,
Sure Ireland's sons will ne'er forget the blood that they have shed;
You may take the shamrock from your hat, and cast it on the sod,
But 'twill take root and flourish there, tho' under foot 'tis trod.
When law can stop the blades of grass from growing as they grow,
And when the leaves in summertime their verdure dare not show,
Then I will change the colour that I wear in my caubeen,
But till that day, please God, I'll stick to wearing of the green.

But if at last our colour should be torn from Ireland's heart,
Her sons, with shame and sorrow, from the dear old isle will part;
I've heard a whisper of a country that lies beyond the sea,
Where rich and poor stand equal in the light of freedom's day.
Oh, Erin! must we leave you, driven by a tyrant's hand?
Must we ask a mother's blessing from a strange and distant land?
Where the cruel cross of England shall nevermore be seen,
And where, please God, we'll live and die still wearing of the green.

THE HARP THAT ONCE THROUGH TARA'S HALLS

Thomas Moore wrote this one in a reproachful vein to stir the spirit of Irish patriotism that for a time seemed too quiescent.

The harp that once through Tara's halls
The soul of music shed,
Now hangs as mute on Tara's walls
As if that soul were fled.

So sleeps the pride of former days,
So glory's thrill is o'er,
And hearts that once beat high for praise
Now feel that praise no more.

No more to chiefs and ladies bright
The harp of Tara swells;
The chord, alone, that breaks at night
Its tale of ruin tells.

Thus Freedom now so seldom wakes,
The only throb she gives
Is when some heart indignant breaks
To show that she still lives.

KILLARNEY

Irish poets kept alive the flame of patriotism, and of all the songs in praise of the country's beauty, this one, written by the nineteenth-century light-opera composer M. W. Balfe, is probably best loved.

By Killarney's lakes and fells,
Em'rald isles and winding bays
Mountain paths and woodland dells,
Mem'ry ever fondly strays.
Bounteous nature loves all lands,
Beauty wanders ev'rywhere,
Footprints leaves on many strands,
But her home is surely there!
Angels fold their wings and rest,
In that Eden of the West,
Beauty's home, Killarney,
Ever fair Killarney.

Innisfallen's ruined shrine
May suggest a passing sigh;
But man's faith can ne'er decline
Such God's wonders floating by.
Castle Lough and Glena bay;
Mountains Tor and Eagle's Nest;
Still at Mucross you must pray,
Though the monks are now at rest.
Angels wonder not that man
There would fain prolong life's span.
Beauty's home, Killarney,
Ever fair Killarney.

DER WACHT AM RHEIN
(The Watch on the Rhine)

The "Tannenbaum" air has served not only for the most famous of German national songs but also for one of the more popular state songs of this country, "Maryland, My Maryland." It was written by Carl Wilhelm. "The Watch on the Rhine" lyric is by Max Schneckenburger.

A voice resounds like thunder peal,
'Mid dashing wave and clang of steel;
"The Rhine, the Rhine, the German Rhine!
Who guards today my stream divine?"

Chorus:
Dear Fatherland! no danger thine, *(Repeat.)*
Firm stand thy sons to watch, to watch the
　　Rhine. *(Repeat.)*
They stand a hundred thousand strong,
Quick to avenge their country's wrong.
With filial love their bosoms swell,
They'll guard the sacred landmark well.

While flows one drop of German blood,
Or sword remains to guard thy flood,
While rifle rests in patriot's hand,
No foe shall tread thy sacred strand!—*Cho.*

Our oath resounds, the river flows,
In golden light our banner glows,
Our hearts will guard thy stream divine,
The Rhine, the Rhine, the German Rhine!
　　　　　　　　　　　　　　—*Cho.*

Es braust ein Ruf wie Donnerhall,
Wie Schwertge klirr und Wogenpralt
Zum Rhein, zum Rhein, zum deutschen
　　Rhein!
Wer will des Stromes Hutersein?—*Cho.*

Durch Hunderttausend zuckt es schnell
Und Aller Augen blitzen hell.
Der Deutsche, kieder, fromm und stark,
Beschutzt die heil'ge Landesmark.—*Cho.*

Chorus:
Lieb Vaterland, magst ruhig sein,
Lieb Vaterland, magst ruhig sein;
Fest steht und treu die Wacht, die Wacht
　　am Rhein!
Fest steht und treu die Wacht, die Wacht
　　am Rhein!

So lang' ein Tropfen Blut noch gluht,
Noch eine Faust den Degen zieht,
Und noch ein Arm die Buchse spannt,
Betritt kein Feind hier deinen Strand.—*Cho.*

Der Schwur erschallt, die Woge rinnt,
Die Fahnen flattern hoch im Wind:
Am Rhein, am Rhein, am deutschen Rhein,
Wir alle wollen Huter sein!—*Cho.*

MEADOWLAND

*This song with music by L. Knipper and Russian lyric by Guser was a favorite
of the Red Army during the revolution. The English translation by M. L. Koor is
from the songbook of Highlander Folk School, Monteagle, Tennessee.*

Meadowland, meadowland,
Meadows green and fields in blossom
Merrily greet the plucky heroes—
Yes, the heroes of the great Red Army.

Maidens fair, why d'you cry?
Blushing maids are sad and weary,
Having to part from handsome lovers,
As the boys are off to join the Army.

Oh, maidens, never fear,
Staunch and faithful are your lovers.
Wish us good speed, for we are leaving
To defend our happy land of Soviets.

Oh, steppeland, vast and free,
Tilled by flourishing kolkhozes,

Everywhere factories and houses,
Newly built, the fruits of Revolution.

Off we go, for we see
Clouds are thickening in the distance.
Makers of war are now preparing
Wantonly to wreck our peaceful labors.

Oh, maidens fair, look at us;
For the foe we are quite ready;
Look at us riding fleet-foot horses,
Driving tanks with engines swift and mighty.

Oh, working folks, peasant folks,
Keep on building, keep on tilling.
Staunchly we hold our constant vigil,
We, the peoples of the land of Soviets.

THE MAPLE LEAF FOREVER

Canada's song by Alexander Muir has no association with war; its lyric celebrates, instead, the beauty of the northern woods.

In days of yore, from Britain's shore,
Wolfe the dauntless hero came,
And planted firm Britannia's flag
On Canada's fair domain.
Here may it wave, our boast and pride,
And join in love together
The Thistle, Shamrock, Rose entwine
The Maple Leaf forever.

Our fair Dominion now extends
From Cape Race to Nootka Sound.
May peace forever be our lot,

And plenteous store abound.
And may those ties of love be ours
Which discord cannot sever;
And flourish green o'er Freedom's home
The Maple Leaf forever.

Chorus:
The Maple Leaf, our emblem dear,
The Maple Leaf forever.
God save our King, and Heaven bless
The Maple Leaf forever.

LA BORINQUEÑA
(Song of Puerto Rico)

Love for a southern island is the theme of this Puerto Rican song with its lyric by M. Fernández written to a traditional air. The English translation is by Jesús Colón and Richard Crosscup. Copyright 1953 by Sing Out! All rights reserved. Used by permission.

Oh, my land of Borinquén! The land where I was born,
Garden so full of flowers, magic'ly wondrous;
Her sky forever luminous is as a dome of light,
While at her feet the placid waves sing so melodious.

When to her shores Columbus came, he cried in joy and wonderment:
"Oh, oh, oh, this is the land of beauty, the land I sought."
Oh, Borinquén, the daughter, the daughter of sea and sun. *(Repeat.)*

La tierra de Borinquén! Donde he nacido yo,
Es un jardin florido, de mágico primor'.
Un cielo siempre nítido, la sirve de dosel,
Y dan arrullos plácidos las olas a sus pies.
Cuando a sus playas llegó Colón, exclamó lleno de admiración,
"Oh, oh, oh, está la linda tierra, que busco yo."
Es Borinquén la hija, la hija del mar y el sol, del mar y el sol, del mar y el sol . . .

BASTA YA!
(That's Enough, Now!)

In another song from Puerto Rico, the island patriotism explodes against Yankee neighbors. Words and music are by Abraham Peña; the English translation is by Arthur Kavess and George Levine. Copyright 1953 by Sing Out! All rights reserved. Used by permission.

Basta ya! Basta ya! Yankee says he's my good neighbor.
From the first faint light of morning to the setting of the sun,
There is no meat for my children, and our only food is rice.
In the sugar fields I labor, but of sugar I have none.
Wall Street bankers take the dollars, Puerto Ricans pay the price.

Chorus:
Basta ya! Basta ya! Basta ya que el yanqui mande,
Desde que amance el día, hasta que se pone el sol,
Mis hijos no comen carne, no comen mas que arroz.

Basta ya! Basta ya! Basta ya que el yanqui mande,
Trabajo todos los días bajo el yugo explotador
Porque los yanquis se llevan el fruto de mi sudor.

In the mansion lives the Yankee, in the slum I'm forced to dwell,
But the men who rule my country tell the people "Go to Hell!"
Now I do not want to govern either New York or Washington,
And I don't want Yankee masters in San Juan or Bayamón.—*Cho.*

I do not want U. S. statehood, colonies are not for me,
What I want is independence—Puerto Rico must be free!
Fifty years the Yanks have ruled us, now at last as one we cry:
Let us stand and fight united, make the Yankee say goodbye!—*Cho.*

El Yanqui vive en el Condado, en el Fanguito estoy yo,
Como ha de vivir el Yanqui mejor en casa que yo.
Yo no quiero la colonia, ni quiero la estadidad,
Yo quiero la independencia como hombre de dignidad.—*Cho.*

Yo no quiero gobernar ni a Washington ni a New York,
No quiero que el Yanqui mande ni en San Juan ni en Bayamón.
Hace ya cincuenta años que el Yanqui dijo que no,
Boricuas todos unidos y verán que dice adiós.—*Cho.*

JANA GANA MANA
(Thou Art the Ruler)

India's independence was won by nonviolence as a policy, based upon religious feeling as expressed in this song by Rabindranath Tagore, who supplied his own English translation.

Thou art the ruler of the minds of all people,
Thou Dispenser of India's destiny,
Thy name rouses the hearts of the Punjab, Sind,
Gujrat and Maratha, of Dravid,
Orissa and Bengal.
It echoes in the hills of
The Vindhyas and Himalayas,
Mingles in the music of
Jumma and Ganges,
And is chanted by the waves
Of the Indian Sea.
They pray for thy blessing
And sing thy praise,
Thou Dispenser of India's destiny,
Victory, Victory, Victory to thee!

Day and night, thy voice goes out
From land to land,
Calling Hindus, Buddhists,
Sikhs and Jains round thy throne
And Parsees, Mussalmans and Christians.
Offerings are brought to thy shrine
By the East and the West
To be woven in a garland of love.
Thou bringest the hearts
Of all peoples into the harmony of one life,

Thou Dispenser of India's destiny,
Victory, Victory, Victory to thee!

Jana-gana-mana adhināyaka jaya hé,
Bhārata bhāgya vidhātā.

Punjāba, Sindhu, Gujarāta, Marāthā,
Drāvida, Utkala, Vangā;
Vindhya, Himācala, Jamunā, Gangā,
Uccala jaladhi tarangā.
Tava śubha nāmé jāgé,
Tava śubha āśisha magé,
Gāhé tava yaśa gāthā.
Janagana mangala dāyaka jaya hé,
Bhārata bhāgya vidhātā;
Jaya hé, jaya hé, jaya hé, jaya jaya jaya jaya hé.

Aharaha tava āhvāna pracārita,
Suni tava udara vānī,
Hindu, Bauddha, Sikha, Jaina, Pārasika,
Musalmāna, Kristānī,
Purava pascima āse
Tava simhāsana pāsé,
Premāhāra hoy gāthā,
Janagana aikya vidhāyaka jaya hé
Bhārata bhāgya vidhātā;
Jaya hé, jaya hé, jaya hé, jaya jaya jaya jaya hé.

AMERICA, THE BEAUTIFUL

Written by Katherine Lee Bates in 1892, with its musical setting supplied by Samuel A. Ward, this song has not lost its charm even today, when a struggle is on to retain the natural beauty it praises.

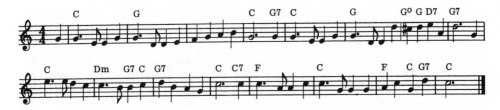

O beautiful for spacious skies, for amber waves of grain,
For purple mountain majesties above the fruited plain.
America! America! God shed His grace on thee,
And crown thy good with brotherhood from sea to shining sea.

O beautiful for pilgrim feet whose stern impassion'd stress
A thoroughfare for freedom beat across the wilderness.
America! America! God mend thy every flaw,
Confirm thy soul in self-control, thy liberty in law.

O beautiful for heroes prov'd in liberating strife,
Who more than self their country loved, and mercy more than life.
America! America! May God thy gold refine
Till all success be nobleness, and every gain divine.

O beautiful for patriot dream that sees beyond the years
Thine alabaster cities gleam, undimmed by human tears.
America! America! God shed His grace on thee
And crown thy good with brotherhood from sea to shining sea.

HATIKVAH   (The Hope)

Long sung in Jewish homes around the world, the promise of a beloved "Sabbath song" was fulfilled when Israel took its place among the nations as a world center for three great religions. Tune and words traditional.

Kol od balevav p'ni ma
Nefesh Yehudi homia,
Ul'faate mizraḥ kadima
Ayin l'Tziyon tzofiya.

Od lo avda tikvatenu,
Hatikva sh'not alpayim,
Lih'yot am ḥofshi b'artzenu,
B'eretz Tziyon virushalayim.

Free translation: So long as the heart of the Jew beats and his eye is turned to the East, so long does our ancient hope of returning to Zion still live.

ROAD TO EILAT
(Hei, Daromah)

With both words and music by Chaim Chafer, this song of Israel reclaimed cele-brates the promise of the new-old land in our own times. The single English verse, intended to convey the feeling of the song as a whole, is by Pete Seeger. Published by Sing Out! *Used by permission.*

To the southward now we travel
Through this land of rock and gravel,
Yet you know just why we sing.
Who'll bring life and grass and water,
Life to raise our sons and daughters,
Youth and life is what we bring.

Chorus:
Hei, daromah, hei daromah,
Hei, daromah, l'Eilat.

Ktsat daromah li'Bersheva
Ruach bamidbar noshevet;
Shvil la aravah yarad.
Laradian im ach miharta,
Et Tel Amar chish avarta,
Vehineh hu chof Eilat.—*Cho.*

Chorus:
Hei daromah, hei daromah,
Hei daromah, l'Eilat.

Hasufa hineh overet
Al haderech hi doheret,
Lamidbar hag'dud shaat,
Jipim kantasim karuach
Halochem rosho paruah
Kan baderech l'Eliat.—*Cho.*

Halochem ahyafe yagayah,
Al haaretz histaraya,
Velchashav hayn kach katoov
Et haaretz Beenish-bati,
Roc la-chem koolah natati
Meeny don vehad yom soof.—*Cho.*

III

WAR SONGS

Songs of all the wars, from the first primitive chant to the latest tape-recorded protest, have assuredly changed the world, though not always in the way intended. The American Revolution, seemingly no more important to Britain at the time than Vietnam to the United States, did not halt the growth of the British Empire but did turn its expansion from west to east. The Civil War did not genuinely emancipate American Negroes but did establish the industrial and financial supremacy of the North. World War I, "the war to end war," failed signally in that purpose but did, in the United States, bring votes for women and the experiment of prohibition, and, in the world, caused not only changes in the map of Europe but emergence of the Americas as new areas of power. World War II did not destroy the Fascist spirit still apparent in the world, but it did improve the condition of Negro Americans, confirm Russian power, and encourage development of power in the Far East.

War songs have expressed the same divergence between war aims and the actual products of war. Always men called on to do the fighting have had their own views and invented their own songs, often very different from popular endorsements of the war sung by the folks back home. Boasts that no one could lick the Kaiser but the red, white, and blue, sentimental ballads about the white cliffs of Dover or the nightingales in Berkeley Square may help sell war bonds but lack the rhythm for long marches. Because home morale is essential too, such World War I songs as "Keep the Home Fires Burning" and "The Long Trail" were indeed important, and would be included here had copyright permissions been obtainable. Certainly we must remember the most popular song of that war, "Tipperary," as successful in this country as in England because Irish boys in London looked also for golden pavements in New York, and all young soldiers thought of the long way home. Other favorites such as "K-K-K-Katy" in World War I and "Lili Marlene" in World War II often were only incidentally connected with war, and were simply songs of their own era liked by the troops. As to war itself, parodies rather than original lyrics often better represented the fighting forces. Some soldier lyrics were true folk songs of combined authorship, varying in different areas or branches of service. Some were topical comments on war's political bombast—

> "We've paid our debt to Lafayette,
> who the hell do we owe now?"

Either way, as they had in common the experienced soldier's frustrations rather than published enthusiasm, it can be argued that the disillusionment with war they represent may yet prove decisive in establishing a genuine peace.

I'LL HANG MY HARP ON A WILLOW TREE

This old song provides the romantic reason for enlistment, according to the stories told ever since the days of Homer. Today, other reasons are clearer, and volunteering less popular, barring exceptional cases. Words and music have been traditional since the days of the troubadours.

I'll hang my harp on a willow tree,
I'm off to the wars again;
My peaceful home has no charm for me,
The battlefield no pain;
The lady I love will soon be a bride,
With a diadem on her brow.
Oh! why did she flatter my boyish pride?
She's going to leave me now.

Then I'll hide in my heart ev'ry selfish care;
The hope of my life I'll resign;
When smiles shall greet the bridal pair,
I'll hasten to give them mine;
I'll laugh and I'll sing though my heart
    may bleed,

And I'll walk in the festive train;
And if I survive it I'll mount my steed
And I'll off to the wars again.

But one golden tress of her hair I'll twine
In my helmet's sable plume,
And then on the field of Palestine
I'll seek an early doom;
And if by the Saracen's hand I fall,
Mid the noble and the brave;
A tear from my lady-love is all
I ask for the warrior's grave.
(Repeat last two lines.)

MARCH OF THE MEN OF HARLECH

This tune, with the Welsh lyric translated by Thomas Love Peacock, is the grimmest of the fighting choruses raised against the Saxons in their conquest of Britain—older and fiercer than the Scottish and Irish songs.

Men of Harlech, in the hollow, do ye hear, like rushing billow,
Wave on wave that surging follow battle's distant sound?
'Tis the tramp of Saxon foemen, Saxon spearmen, Saxon bowmen,
Be they knights or hinds or yeomen, they shall bite the ground!
Loose the folds asunder, flag we conquer under!
The placid sky now bright on high shall launch its bolts of thunder.
Onward, 'tis our country needs us, he is bravest, he who leads us,
Honor's self now proudly heads us, Freedom, God, and Right!

Rocky steeps and passes narrow flash with spear and flight of arrow,
Who would think of death or sorrow? Death is glory now!
Hurl the reeling horsemen over, let the earth dead foemen cover;
Fate of friend or wife or lover trembles on a blow.
Strands of life are riven, blow for blow is given,
In deadly lock or battle shock, and mercy shrieks to heaven!
Men of Harlech! Young or hoary would you win a name in story,
Strike for home, for life, for glory, Freedom, God, and Right!

THE BRITISH GRENADIERS

Catchiest of marching tunes, this one must have led many a youth to take the king's shilling. Origin of the sixteenth-century tune is unknown; the lyric dates from the reign of James II.

Some talk of Alexander, and some of Hercules,
Of Hector and Lysander and such great names as these.
But of all the world's brave heroes, there's none that can compare
With a tow, row, row, row, row, row, to the British Grenadier.

Whene'er we are commanded to storm the palisades,
Our leaders march with fusées, and we with hand grenades.
We throw them from the glacis, about the enemy's ears,
With a tow, etc.

And when the siege is over, we to the town repair;
The townsmen cry, "Hurra, boys, here comes a Grenadier;
Here come the Grenadiers, my boys, who know no doubts and fears!"
With a tow, etc.

Then let us fill a bumper, and drink a health to those
Who carry caps and pouches, and wear the loupèd clothes.
May they and their commanders live happy all their years,
With a tow, etc.

MALBROUGH S'EN VA-T'EN GUERRE
(Malbrough Has Gone to Battle)

The old French song marking triumph over an early Churchill hopefully chronicles the death of a general who, in fact, did not die in battle. (Later, in England, the tune became "We Won't Go Home Till Morning!")

Malbrough has gone to battle,	Malbrough s'en va-t'en guerre,
Mironton, mironton, mirontaine.	Mironton, mironton, mirontaine.
Who knows when he'll return?	Ne sait qu'on reviendra,
Who knows when he'll return	Ne sait qu'on reviendra,
Or will be seen again?	Ou s'il reviendra pas.

He'll surely come in springtime
Mironton, etc.
He'll surely come in springtime
Upon a holy day.

Il reviendra-z-à Pâques,
Mironton, etc.
Il reviendra-z-à Pâques
Ou à la Trinité.

The spring is past and gone,
Mironton, etc.
The spring is past and gone,
Malbrough does not return.

La Trinité se passe,
Mironton, etc.
La Trinité se passe,
Malbrough ne revient pas.

Madame climbs to her tower,
Mironton, etc.
Madame climbs to her tower
As high as she can climb.

Madame à sa tour monte,
Mironton, etc.
Madame à sa tour monte
Si haut qu'ell' peut monter.

She sees approach her page,
Mironton, mironton, mirontaine.
She sees approach her page,
All dressed in mourning black.

Elle aperçoit son page,
Mironton, etc.
Elle aperçoit son page
Tout de noir habillé.

My page—ah, come, my page
Mironton, etc.
My page—come, pretty page
And say what news you bring.

Beau page, ah! mon beau page,
Mironton, etc.
Beau page, ah! mon beau page,
Quell' nouvelle apportez?

At news I must reveal,
Mironton, etc.
At news I must reveal
Milady's tears will flow.

Aux nouvell's que j'apporte,
Mironton, etc.
Aux nouvell's que j'apporte,
Vos beaux yeux vont pleurer.

Put off your silks and satins,
Mironton, etc.
Put off your silks and satins,
Wear no more rose brocade.

Quittez vos habits roses,
Mironton, etc.
Quittez vos habits roses,
Et vos satins brochés.

For Malbrough, ma'am, is dead—
Mironton, etc.
Milady's lord is dead,
Is dead and buriéd.

Monsieur d'Malbrough est mort,
Mironton, etc.
Monsieur d'Malbrough est mort,
Est mort et enterré.

YANKEE DOODLE

Beginning in England as a Roundhead song in Cromwell's revolution, this song about an unheroic "Yankee Doodle dandy" with a feather in his cap stood for foreign, un-English influence among the royalists. Brought to America, the catchy tune inspired new verses, and was played by the victors at Yorktown.

Father and I went down to camp, along with Captain Good'in,
And there we saw the men and boys as thick as hasty puddin'.

Chorus:
Yankee Doodle, keep it up, Yankee Doodle dandy.
Mind the music and the step, and with the girls be handy.

And there we see a thousand men, as rich as Squire David,
And what they wasted every day, I wish it could be savèd.—*Cho.*

And there was Captain Washington upon a strapping stallion,
A-giving orders to his men; I guess there was a million.—*Cho.*

And then the feathers on his hat, they looked so very fine, ah!
I wanted peskily to get to give to my Jemima.—*Cho.*

And there I see a swamping gun, large as a log of maple,
Upon a mighty little cart; a load for father's cattle.—*Cho.*

And every time they fired it off, it took a horn of powder;
It made a noise like father's gun, only a nation louder.—*Cho.*

And there I see a little keg, its head all made of leather,
They knocked upon't with little sticks, to call the folks together.—*Cho.*

And Cap'n Davis had a gun, he kind o' clapt his hand on't
And stuck a crooked stabbing-iron upon the little end on't.—*Cho.*

The troopers, too, would gallop up and fire right in our faces;
It scared me almost half to death to see them run such races.—*Cho.*

It scared me so I hooked it off, nor stopped, as I remember,
Nor turned about till I got home, locked up in mother's chamber.—*Cho.*

THE BLUE BELLS OF SCOTLAND

Alas that men must fight and women must weep; among the Scottish songs, this one written by a woman, Mrs. James Grant, tells of the strain of war as felt by those left to wait at home.

Oh! where, tell me where is your Highland laddie gone?
Oh! where, tell me where is your Highland laddie gone?
He's gone with streaming banners where noble deeds are done,
And it's oh, in my heart I wish him safe at home.

Oh! where, tell me where did your Highland laddie dwell?
Oh! where, tell me where did your Highland laddie dwell?
He dwelt in bonnie Scotland, where blooms the sweet blue bell,
And it's oh, in my heart I lo'e my laddie well.

Oh! what, tell me what if your Highland lad be slain?
Oh! what, tell me what if your Highland lad be slain?
Oh, no! true love will be his guard, and bring him safe again.
For it's oh, my heart would break if my Highland lad were slain.

LA MARSEILLAISE

When Claude Rouget de Lisle wrote it in 1792, France was fighting invasion, and refusing, as a later lyric would put it, to "bow down to Burgundy." Although played to welcome revolution at the Finland station, it began as a war song calling for enemy blood.

Arise, ye sons of France, to glory!
Your day of freedom bids you rise!
Your children, wives and grandsires hoary—
Behold their tears, and hear their cries!
Behold their tears, and hear their cries.

Allons, enfants de la patrie,
Le jour de gloire est arrivé.
Contre nous de la tyrannie
L'étendard sanglant est levé.
Entendez vous dans les campagnes

Shall hateful tyrants, mischief breeding,
With hireling hosts, a ruffian band,
Affright and desolate the land
While peace and liberty lie bleeding?
To arms, ye sons of France!
To arms, your ranks advance!
March on, march on! All hearts resolved
On liberty or death!

Mugir ces féroces soldats?
Ils viennent jusque dans nos bras
Egorger vos fils, vos compagnes:
Aux armes, Citoyens!
Formez vos bataillons,
Marchons, marchons,
Qu'un sang impur
Abreuve nos sillons!

THE GIRL I LEFT BEHIND ME

Though mention of "the moor" and "Brighton camp" proclaims its British origin, this song was the sort to be popular with Americans during the revolution. The tune is traditional; the words are by Samuel Lover, the Irish novelist.

I'm lonesome since I crossed the hill,
And o'er the moor and valley;
Such heavy thoughts my heart do fill,
Since parting with my Sally.
I seek no more the fine and gay,
For each doth but remind me
How swift the hours did pass away
With the girl I've left behind me.

Oh, ne'er shall I forget the night,
The stars were bright above me,
And gently lent their silv'ry light,
When first she vowed she loved me.
But now I'm bound to Brighton camp,
Kind heaven, may favor find me,
And send me safely back again
To the girl I've left behind me.

The bee shall honey taste no more,
The dove become a ranger,
The dashing waves shall cease to roar,
Ere she's to me a stranger.
The vows we registered above
Shall ever cheer and bind me,
In constancy to her I love,
The girl I've left behind me.

My mind her form shall still retain,
In sleeping or in waking,
Until I see my love again,
For whom my heart is breaking.
If ever I should see the day
When Mars shall have resigned me,
For evermore I'll gladly stay
With the girl I've left behind me.

JOHN BROWN'S BODY

The death of a hero has sparked many wars and revolutions, and the song about the Civil War martyr deserves its fame if only as inspiration for the "Battle Hymn of the Republic." Lesser parodies are endless; southern soldiers sang "Hang Abe Lincoln on a Sour Apple Tree," while the Yankees sang "Hang Jeff Davis." Prohibitionists would write a "Temperance Battle Hymn." Today's militant poor sing "Move on Over," Len Chandler's lyric following the original song credited to William Staffe.

John Brown's body lies a-mould'ring in the grave,
John Brown's body lies a-mould'ring in the grave,
John Brown's body lies a-mould'ring in the grave,
His soul is marching on!

Chorus:
Glory, glory, hallelujah!   Glory, glory, hallelujah!
Glory, glory, hallelujah!   His soul is marching on!

The stars of heaven are looking kindly down,
On the grave of old John Brown!—*Cho.*

He's gone to be a soldier in the army of th
Lord!
His soul is marching on.—*Cho.*

John Brown's knapsack is strapped upon h
back!
His soul is marching on.—*Cho.*

(Second Version)

Old John Brown lies a-mouldering in the grave,
Old John Brown lies slumbering in his grave—
But John Brown's soul is marching with the brave,
His soul is marching on.

Chorus:
Glory, glory, hallelujah!   Glory, glory, hallelujah!
Glory, glory, hallelujah!   His soul is marching on.

He has gone to be a soldier in the army of th
Lord,
He is sworn as a private in the ranks of th
Lord—
He shall stand at Armageddon with his brav
old sword,
When Heaven is marching on.
Glory, glory, hallelujah, etc.
For Heaven is marching on.

MOVE ON OVER *Sung to* "John Brown's Body"

Mine eyes have seen injustice in each city, town and state
Your jails are filled with black men and your courts are white with hate.
And with every bid for freedom someone whispers to us wait
That's why we keep marching on.

Chorus:
Move on over or we'll move on over you
Move on over or we'll move on over you
Move on over or we'll move on over you
And the movement's moving on.

You conspire to keep us silent in the field and in the slum
You promise us the vote then sing us We Shall Overcome

But John Brown knew what freedom was and died to win us some
That's why we keep marching on.

It is you who are subversive, you're the kille of the dream
In a savage world of bandits it is you w are extreme.
You never take your earmuffs off nor listen when we scream
That's why we keep marching on.

I declare my independence from the fool a from the knave
I declare my independence from the cowa and the slave

I declare that I will fight for right and fear
no jail nor grave
That's why we keep marching on.

Many noble dreams are dreamed by small
and voiceless men

Many noble deeds are done the righteous to
defend
We're here today, John Brown, to say we'll
triumph in the end
That's why we keep marching on.

BATTLE HYMN OF THE REPUBLIC

*When Julia Ward Howe wrote new words for the "brave music" of "John Brown's
Body," she sold her lyric to the* Atlantic Monthly *for four dollars. Her song be-
came a request number for Lincoln; in World War II it was sung in Westminster
Abbey. The tune was borrowed for the labor song "Solidarity Forever," and
British explorers sang Mrs. Howe's words in camp at the foot of Mount Everest.
Lately, the lyric was parodied for peace in Vietnam ("Gory, gory, gory, what a
helluva way to die,") and sung by dissenters at the 1968 Democratic convention.*

Mine eyes have seen the glory of the coming of the Lord;
He is trampling out the vintage where the grapes of wrath are stored;
He hath loosed the fateful lightning of His terrible swift sword,
His truth is marching on.

Chorus:
Glory! glory! Hallelujah!
Glory! glory! Hallelujah!
Glory! glory! Hallelujah!
His truth is marching on.

I have seen Him in the watchfires of a hundred circling camps;
They have builded Him an altar in the evening dews and damps;
I can read His righteous sentence by the dim and flaring lamps,
His day is marching on.—*Cho.*

He has sounded forth the trumpet that shall never call retreat;
He is sifting out the hearts of men before His judgment seat;
Oh, be swift, my soul, to answer Him, be jubilant, my feet!
Our God is marching on.—*Cho.*

MARCHING THROUGH GEORGIA

*This favorite Yankee tune of the Civil War was, with the best of intentions,
played to welcome southern troops landing in Ireland during World War I. Hap-
pily, no serious incident occurred, despite southern feeling about Sherman's
march to the sea. Words by Henry C. Work.*

Bring the good old bugle, boys, we'll sing another song,
Sing it with a spirit that will start the world along,
Sing it as we used to sing it, fifty thousand strong,
While we were marching through Georgia.

How the turkeys gobbled which our commissary found,
How the sweet potatoes even started from the ground,
How the darkies shouted when they heard the joyful sound
While we, etc.

"Sherman's dashing Yankee boys will never reach the coast!"
So the saucy rebels said, and 'twas a handsome boast
Had they not forgot, alas, to reckon with the host,
While we, etc.

Sixty miles in latitude, three hundred to the main;
Treason fled before us for resistance was in vain,
So we made a thoroughfare for Freedom and her train,
While we, etc.

TRAMP! TRAMP! TRAMP!

Its success with the Union Army may have been due to the march rhythm rather than to the somewhat sentimental lyric by George F. Root. But the music served later wars; in the 1898 war with Spain, American entrance into the colonial field developed a famous parody:

> *"And beneath the starry flag*
> *Civilize 'em with a Krag."*

In the prison cell I sit, thinking, mother dear, of you,
And our bright and happy home so far away;
And the tears they fill my eyes, spite of all that I can do,
Though I try to cheer my comrades and be gay.

Tramp! tramp! tramp! the boys are marching,
Cheer up, comrades, they will come.
And beneath the starry flag we shall breathe the air again
Of the free land in our own beloved home.

In the battle front we stood, when their fiercest charge they made,
And they swept us off, a hundred men or more;
But before we reached their lines, they were beaten back, dismayed,
And we heard the cry of vict'ry o'er and o'er.—*Cho.*

TENTING TONIGHT

Though a Civil War song, this one reflects a disillusionment with fighting that would become more common in the songs of later wars. The composer was Walter Kittredge.

We're tenting tonight on the old camp
    ground,
Give us a song to cheer
Our weary hearts, a song of home,
And friends we love so dear.

Chorus:
Many are the hearts that are weary tonight,
Wishing for the war to cease;
Many are the hearts looking for the right,
To see the dawn of peace.
Tenting tonight, tenting tonight,
Tenting on the old camp ground.

We've been tenting tonight on the old camp
    ground,
Thinking of days gone by

Of the loved ones at home that gave us
    the hand,
And the tear that said "good-bye!"—*Cho.*

We are tired of war on the old camp ground,
Many are dead and gone,
Of the brave and true wh've left their homes,
Others been wounded long.—*Cho.*

We've been fighting today on the old camp
    ground,
Many are lying near;
Some are dead and some are dying;
Many are in tears.

Many are the hearts, etc.
Dying tonight, dying tonight,
Dying on the old camp ground.

DIXIE

Starting as a Civil War song, "Dixie" still brings rebel yells and brought southern audiences to hysteria when Toscanini led it during the "cold civil war" of our time. Emmett's words are debatable: does "Dixie" mean below the Mason-Dixon Line, or did it refer to the worthless banknotes called "dixies"? Does "look away" mean a reference to the underground railway? Good southerners listen loyally, whistle, and look away.

I wish I was in de land ob cotton,
Old times dar am not forgotten,
Look away, Look away! Look away! Dixie
    Land.
In Dixie Land whar I was born in,
Early on one frosty mornin',
Look away, Look away! Look away! Dixie
    Land.

Chorus:
Den I wish I was in Dixie, Hooray! Hooray!
In Dixie Land I'll take my stand,
To lib and die in Dixie.
Away, Away, Away down South in Dixie.
                                    (Repeat)

Old Missus marry "Will-de-weaber,"
Willyum was a gay deceaber;
Look away, etc.
But when he put his arm around 'er,
He smiled as fierce as a forty pounder.
Look away, etc.

His face was sharp as a butcher's cleaber,
But dat did not seem to greab 'er;
Look away, etc.
Old Missus acted de foolish part,
And died for a man dat broke her heart.
Look away, etc.

Now here's health to the next old Missus,
An' all the gals dat want to kiss us;
Look away, etc.
But if you want to drive 'way sorrow,
Come and hear dis song tomorrow.
Look away, etc.

Dar's buckwheat cakes and Injun batter,
Makes you fat or a little fatter;
Look away, etc.
Den hoe it down an' scratch your grabble,
To Dixie's Land I'm bound to trabble.
Look away, etc.

THE BONNIE BLUE FLAG

Actually, like the Stars and Stripes, the Confederate flag was red, white, and blue. But this southern song ran second only to "Dixie" in popularity, and its enumeration of the seceding states was an honor roll cherished by diehards long after the war's end. The composer was Harry McCarthy.

We are a band of brothers, and native to the soil,
Fighting for the property we gained by honest toil;
And when our rights were threatened, the cry rose near and far,
Hurrah for the Bonnie Blue Flag that bears a Single Star.

Chorus:
Hurrah! Hurrah! For Southern Rights, Hurrah!
Hurrah! for the Bonnie Blue Flag, that bears a Single Star.

As long as the old Union was faithful to her trust,
Like friends and like brothers, kind were we and just.
But now, when Northern treachery attempts our rights to mar,
We hoist on high the Bonnie Blue Flag that bears a Single Star.

Chorus:
Hurrah! Hurrah! For Southern rights hurrah!
Hurrah! for the Bonnie Blue Flag has gain'd th' Eleventh Star.

First, gallant South Carolina nobly made the stand;
Then came Alabama, who took her by the hand;
Next, quickly Mississippi, Georgia and Florida,
All rais'd on high the Bonnie Blue Flag that bears a Single Star.—*Cho.*

Ye men of valor, gather round the Banner of the Right,
Texas and fair Louisiana join us in the fight;
Davis, our loved President, and Stephens, statesman rare,
Now rally round the Bonnie Blue Flag that bears a Single Star.—*Cho.*

And here's to brave Virginia! the Old Dominion State
With the young Confederacy at length has linked her fate;
Impell'd by her example, now other states prepare
To hoist on high the Bonnie Blue Flag that bears a Single Star.—*Cho.*

Then here's to our Confederacy, strong we are and brave,
Like patriots of old, we'll fight our heritage to save;
And rather than submit to shame, to die we would prefer,
So cheer for the Bonnie Blue Flag that bears a Single Star.—*Cho.*

Then cheer, boys, cheer, raise the joyous shout,
For Arkansas and North Carolina now have both gone out;
And let another rousing cheer for Tennessee be given—
The Single Star of the Bonnie Blue Flag has grown to be Eleven.—*Cho.*

WHEN THIS CRUEL WAR IS OVER

With suitable changes, this song was popular on both sides in the War Between the States. Here the Confederate version, with its "suit of gray," could of course read "a suit of blue" with the rhyming line perhaps altered to read "Ever to be true." Words by Charles C. Sawyer, music by Harry Tucker.

Dearest one, do you remember when we last did meet?
When you told me how you loved me, kneeling at my feet?
Oh! how proud you stood before me, in your suit of gray;
When you vowed from me and country ne'er to go astray!

Chorus:
Weeping, sad and lonely, sighs and tears, how vain;
When this cruel war is over, praying then to meet again!

When the summer breeze is sighing mournfully along;
Or when autumn leaves are falling, sadly breathes the song.
Oft in dreams I see you lying on the battle plain;
Lonely, wounded, even dying, calling, but in vain.—*Cho.*

If amid the din of battle, nobly you should fall;
Far away from those who love you, none to hear you call;
Who would whisper words of comfort? Who would soothe your pain?
Such are many cruel fancies, ever in my brain!—*Cho.*

WHEN JOHNNY COMES MARCHING HOME

Now he is a hero, and his song belongs to all the wars. Paul S. Gilmore, the famous bandmaster, wrote this one.

When Johnny comes marching home again, Hurrah, hurrah!
We'll give him a hearty welcome then, Hurrah, hurrah!
The men will cheer, the boys will shout,

The ladies, they will all turn out,
And we'll all feel gay when Johnny comes marching home.

The old church bell will peal with joy, Hurrah, hurrah!
To welcome home our darling boy, Hurrah, hurrah!
The village lads and lassies say,
With roses they will strew the way,
And we'll all feel gay when Johnny comes marching home.

Get ready for the jubilee, Hurrah, hurrah!
We'll give the hero three times three, Hurrah, hurrah!
The laurel wreath is ready now
To place upon his loyal brow;
And we'll all feel gay when Johnny comes marching home.

COMRADES

This was the popular song of the war with Spain, which in '98 claimed those foot-
loose young men who were not joining the gold rush. With San Juan Hill in the
headlines, while "manhood was dawning" in Felix McLennon's lyric, the United
States was flexing muscles and finding the first idealistic reasons for the first war to
unite North and South against a distant foe. "Comrades" is a song for soldiers too
young to count casualties from typhoid and bad rations.

Comrades, comrades, ever since we were boys,
Sharing each other's sorrows, sharing each other's joys.
Comrades when manhood was dawning, faithful whate'er might betide—
When danger threatened, my jolly old comrade was there by my side.

A HOT TIME IN THE OLD TOWN TONIGHT

Here was the song hit for the soldiers in that war of '98—light-hearted lads who
had not heard of napalm. The composer, Theodore Metz, credited a minstrel
singer with the words. The Spanish considered it our national anthem.

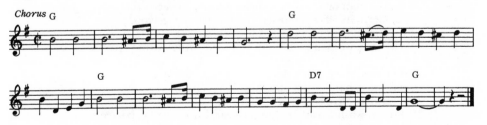

When you hear dem a bells go ding, ling ling,
All join 'round and sweetly you must sing,
And when the verse am through, in the chorus all join in—
There'll be a hot time in the old town tonight.

OVER THERE

In World War I, George M. Cohan's song hit did everything that a composer born on the Fourth of July could wish, but not everyone whistling his tune caught the pun in the first notes of the chorus, which are those of the whippoor-will—that is, "Beat Kaiser Bill." Copyright 1917 (renewed) by Leo Feist, Inc., New York. Used by permission.

Over there, over there,
Send the word, send the word over there
That the Yanks are coming, the Yanks are
    coming,
The drums rum-tumming everywhere.

So prepare, say a pray'r,
Send the word, send the word to beware—
We'll be over, we're coming over,
And we won't come back till it's over
    over there.

MADEMOISELLE FROM ARMENTIÈRES
(Hinky Dinky, Parlee-Voo)

Some say Mam'selle was real, and refused to kiss a general. Legionnaires still love the song, in endless variants, but no one knows whom to credit; the tune is said to have been borrowed from the French.

Two German officers crossed the Rhine, parlee-voo,
Two German officers crossed the Rhine, parlee-voo,
Two German officers crossed the Rhine
To kiss the women and drink the wine, hinky dinky, parlee-voo.

Oh farmer, have you a daughter fair, parlee-voo,
Oh farmer, have you a daughter fair, parlee-voo,
Oh farmer, have you a daughter fair
Who can wash a soldier's underwear, hinky dinky, parlee-voo.

Mademoiselle from Armentières, parlee-voo,
Mademoiselle from Armentières, parlee-voo,
Mademoiselle from Armentières
She ain't even heard of underwear, hinky dinky, parlee-voo.

QUAND MADELON

Both for French troops and for Americans who landed in France, this was the marching song of World War I. Written by Louis Bousquet and Camille Robert; copyright 1917 by Mills Music, Inc. All rights reserved. Used by permission.

Quand Madelon vient nous servir à boire,
Sous la tonnelle on frôle son jupon,
Et chacun lui raconte une histoire,
Une histoire à sa façon.
La Madelon pour nous n'est pas sévère,
Quand on lui prend la taille ou le menton,
Elle rit, c'est tout l'mal qu'ell' sait faire,
Madelon, Madelon, Madelon!

When Madelon comes bringing us the wine,
As we sit waiting in the cabaret
Every man has his private design—
Has a hope, makes a pass, says his say.
Our Madelon will never scold or fuss,
She never frowns or cries non, non, non, non!
She laughs, that's the way she has with us—
Madelon, Madelon, Madelon!

AROUND HER NECK SHE WORE A YELLOW RIBBON

A genuine folk song of undetermined origin, this one was revived for World War I. The original purple ribbon was changed to yellow for the cavalry, which retained its dash in that war although saber charges were over.

Around her neck she wore a yellow ribbon,
She wore it in December and in the month of May,
And if you asked her why the decoration,
She said 'twas for her lover who was far, far away.

Far away, far away—she wore it for a soldier who was far, far away.

Above a grave she scattered yellow flowers,
She brought them in December and in the month of May.
And if you asked her why she came to bring them,
She said 'twas for a soldier who was six feet away.

BUGLE CALLS

Although a Berlin song threatened to murder the bugler, recruits lacking an ear for music found it easier to remember the calls with the suitable lyrics they made up. These antedated the world wars but can still be heard wherever bugles blow.

(Reveille)

(Mess Call)

(Taps)

(Reveille)

I can't get 'em up, I can't get 'em up,
I can't get 'em up in the morning.
I can't get 'em up, I can't get 'em up,
I can't get 'em up at all.

The corp'ral's worse'n the privates,
The sergeant's worse'n the corporal,
Lieutenant's worse'n the sergeant,
And the captain's the worst of 'em all!

(Mess Call)

Soupy, soupy, soupy, without any beans
Coffee, coffee, coffee, without any cream,
Porky, porky, porky, with no streak o' lean.

(Taps)

Good night, go to sleep,
Go to sleep, go to sleep,
Go to sleeeeep, go to sleep, good night.

ANCHORS AWEIGH

The Navy song has a proper seafaring swing, with music credited to Captain Alfred H. Mills and Charles A. Zimmerman. If not all sailors are college men, as the second verse seems to suggest, you have to allow this branch of the service its share of swank.

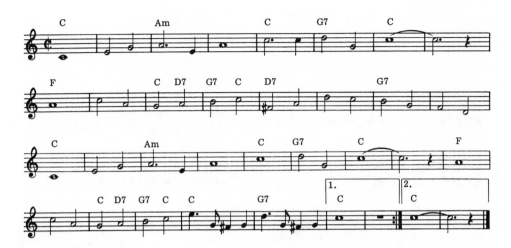

Stand Navy out to sea,
Fight our battle cry.
We'll never change our course, so
Vicious foe steer shy—y—y—y.
Roll out the T.N.T.
Anchors aweigh—
Sail on to victory
And sink their bones to Davy Jones, hooray.

Anchors aweigh, my boys,
Anchors aweigh.
Farewell to college joys,
We sail at break of day—ay—ay—ay.
Through our last night on shore,
Drink to the foam.
Until we meet again,
Here's wishing you a happy voyage home.

THE MARINES' HYMN
(Halls of Montezuma)

A memorable tune plus a gibe at rival services in the last two lines—what more could a landing force ask? This one has all the appropriate assurance.

From the halls of Montezuma to the shores of Tripoli,
We fight our country's battles on the land and on the sea.
First to fight for right and freedom, and to keep our honor clean,
We are proud to claim the title of United States Marines.

Our flag's unfurled to every breeze from dawn to setting sun;
We have fought in every clime and place where we could take a gun;
In the snow of far-off northern lands and in sunny tropic scenes;
You will find us always on the job, the United States Marines.

Here's a health to you and to our corps, which we are proud to serve;
In many a strife we've fought for life, and never lost our nerve.
If the Army and the Navy ever looked on heaven's scenes,
They would find the streets are guarded by United States Marines.

ARTILLERY SONG (The Caissons)

The cannon wheels go rolling through this one in good time, and if modern wars are fought with missiles, we still have old-model hardware on hand.

Over hill, over dale, we have hit the dusty trail,
And our caissons go rolling along.
In and out, hear them shout: "Counter march! And right about,"
And the caissons go rolling along.

Then, it's Hi, hi, hee! In the field artillery,
Shout out your numbers good and strong (one, two!)
Where'er you go, you will always know,
That those caissons go rolling along (keep them rolling),
That those caissons go rolling along.

In the storm, in the night, action left or action right,
See the caissons go rolling along.
Limber front, limber rear, prepare to mount your cannoneer,
And the caissons go rolling along.

Was it high, was it low, where the hell did that one go?
As those caissons go rolling along.
Was it left, was it right, now we won't get home tonight,
As those caissons go rolling along.

THE HANDSOME YOUNG AIRMAN

Last of the single-combat heroes, the fighter pilot's song is appropriately tough; and his fate in World War I, when he flew the "flying coffins" over France, was frequently as described in this British song.

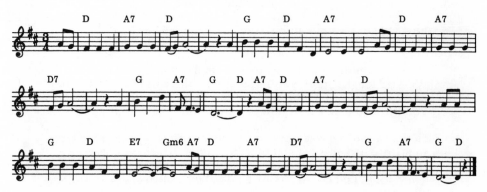

A handsome young airman lay dying,
And as on the airdrome he lay,
To mechanics who 'round him came sighing
These last parting words he did say:

"Take the cylinders out of my kidneys,
The connecting rods out of my brain,
The crankshaft out of my backbone,
And assemble the engine again."

FIDDLERS' GREEN

In this ghost song for the vanished cavalry, at least the other services get mentioned. Author and composer are nameless, and the song, to judge from its content, must be at least as old as the Indian wars.

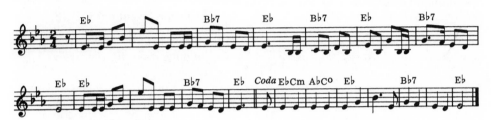

Halfway down the road to hell,
In a shady meadow green,
Are the souls of all dead troopers camped
Near a good old-time canteen.
And this eternal resting place
Is known as Fiddlers' Green.

Though some go curving down the trail
To seek a warmer scene,
No trooper ever gets to hell
Ere he's emptied his canteen,
And so rides back to drink again
With friends at Fiddlers' Green.

And so when man and horse go down
Beneath a saber keen,
Or in a roaring charge or fierce melee
You stop a bullet clean,
And the hostiles come to get your scalp,
Just empty your canteen,
And put your pistol to your head
And go to Fiddlers' Green.

Marching past, straight through to hell,
The Infantry are seen,
Accompanied by the Engineers,
Artillery and Marine,
For none but the shades of Cavalrymen
Dismount at Fiddlers' Green.

THE BELLS OF HELL . . .

This one originated with the British in World War I and was a Royal Flying Corps favorite, although doubtless the other services shared its sentiments, as did an American who sent it home.

The bells of hell go ting-a-ling-a-ling
For you but not for me;
For me the angels sing-a-ling-a-ling,
They've got the goods for me.

O Death, where is thy sting-a-ling-a-ling,
O grave, thy victory?
The bells of hell go ting-a-ling-a-ling,
For you but not for me!

CAPTAIN JINKS

This cheerful nonsense ditty of the Civil War period was a great hit in its day, and survived for later singing. The words were written by William Horace Lingard, the music by T. Mackagan.

I'm Captain Jinks of the horse marines,
I feed my horse on corn and beans,
And though I live beyond my means,
I'm a captain in the Army.

I joined my corps when twenty-one,
Of course I thought it capital fun,

When the enemy came, of course I'd run,
For I'm not cut out for the Army.

The first time I went out to drill,
The bugle sounding made me ill;
Of the battlefield I've had my fill,
For I'm not cut out for the Army.

WHERE THEY WERE

A product of World War I, this one needs no explanation as to theme, and perhaps the writers preferred anonymity to credit. Or, like a folk song, it just grew, with help from several sources.

If you want to know where the Gen'rals were,
I'll tell you where they were,
I'll tell you where they were,
Yes—I'll tell you where they were.
Oh, if you want to know where the Gen'rals
were,
I'll tell you where they were;
Back in gay Paree!
Spoken: How do you know?

Chorus:
I saw them! I saw them!
Back in gay Paree I saw them,
Back in gay Paree!

If you want to know where the Colonels were
I'll tell you where they were,
I'll tell you where they were,
Yes--I'll tell you where they were.
Oh, if you want to know where the Colonels
were,

I'll tell you where they were;
Way behind the lines!

Chorus:
I saw them! I saw them!
Way behind the lines I saw them,
Way behind the lines.

If you want to know where the Majors were,
Etc., etc.
Playing with the mademoiselles, etc.

If you want to know where the Captains were,
Etc., etc.
Down in the deep dugout, etc.

If you want to know where the Sergeants were,
Etc., etc.
Drinking up the Private's rum, etc.

If you want to know where the Privates were,
Etc., etc.
Up to their necks in mud! etc.

BOMBED!

Also belonging to World War I, or to those "brush-fire wars" lightly regarded at home, is the bombing of troops described in this song of British troops under fire in World War I. Now it hardly counts if bombs miss the backyard.

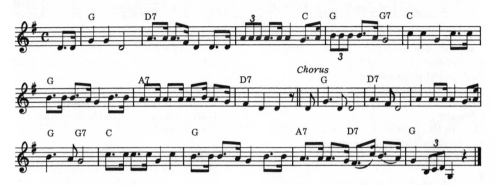

We were bombed last night, bombed the night before,
And we're gonna be bombed tonight as we never were bombed before.
When we're bombed, we're scared as we can be;
They can bomb the whole darn army if they don't bomb me.

Chorus:
They're over us, over us, one little cave for the four of us.
Glory be to God, there are no more of us, or they'd surely bomb the whole darn
    crew.

I WANT TO GO HOME

"It worried the French—they took it seriously," said the young lieutenant who brought this one back from World War I. Credits are uncertain; the First Division knew it, but the First Canadian contingent claims it too.

I want to go home, I want to go home.
Shrapnel and whizzbangs and pipsqueaks
    galore,
I don't want to go to the trenches no more.
Far over the sea, where the Germans can't
    get after me—
Oh, my, I'm too young to die.
I want to go home.

I want to go home, I want to go home.
The war ain't so bad if you're wearin' a star
But bein' a private don't get you so far.
I want to go home, I want to go home—
Oh, my, I'm too young to die.
I want to go home.

THE PEAT BOG SOLDIERS   (Wir Sind Die Moorsoldaten)

Between the world wars, songs sung in the "rehearsal" for World War II—the civil war in Spain—came out of the concentration camps. This one, banned in Nazi Germany, was sung in Spain. The tune is old, the author unknown.

Far and wide as the eye can wander,
Heath and bog are everywhere.
Not a bird sings out to cheer us,
Oaks are standing gaunt and bare.

Chorus:
We are the peat bog soldiers;
We're marching with our spades
To the bog.

Up and down the guards are pacing,
No one, no one can go through.
Flight would mean a sure death-facing,
Guns and barbed wire greet our view.—*Cho.*

But for us there is no complaining,
Winter will in time be past;

One day we shall cry rejoicing,
"Homeland dear, you're mine at last!"

Chorus:
Then will the peat bog soldiers
March no more with their spades
To the bog!

Wohin auch das Auge blicket,
Moor und Heide nur ringsum.
Vogelsang uns nicht erquicket,
Eichen stehen kahl und krumm.

Chorus:
Wir sind die Moorsoldaten,
Wir ziehen mit dem Spaten
Ins Moor.

FREIHEIT (Freedom)

A great song for stouthearted singers, this one was taken to Spain by anti-Nazi members of the famous International Brigade. Words by Karl Ernst, set to music by Peter Daniel.

Spanish heavens spread their brilliant starlight
High above our trenches in the plain.
From the distance morning comes to greet us,
Calling us to battle once again.

Chorus:
Far off is our land,
Yet ready we stand.
We're fighting and winning for you,
Freedom!

Spaniens Himmel breitet seine
Sterne Über unsre Schlutengräben aus;
Und der Morgen grüsst schon aus der Ferne
Bald geht es zum neuen Kampf hinaus.

Chorus:
Die Heimat ist weit,
Doch wir sind Bereit,
Wir kämpfen und siegen für dich,
Freiheit!

VIVA LA QUINCE BRIGADA
(Long Live the Fifteenth Brigade)

The Fifteenth Brigade was the international one, which had its own song in English but learned enough Spanish to join in this rewrite of an old Spanish folk song.

Long live the Fifteenth Brigade,
Rhumbala, rhumbala, rhumbala. *(Repeat.)*
Who have covered themselves with glory,
Ay Manuela, Ay Manuela.

We fight against the Moors, the fascist
    mercenaries.
Our only wish is to finish
Forever with the fascists.
On the Jarama front, we have no planes,
    no tanks, no cannon—
Ay Manuela, Ay Manuela.

Yet we shall go from Spain
To fight on other fronts.

Viva la Quince Brigada,
Rhumbala, rhumbala, rhumbala. *(Repeat.)*
Que se ha cubierta de gloria,
Ay Manuela, Ay Manuela.

Luchamos contra los Morros (Rhumbala, *etc.*)
Mercenarios y fascistas (Rhumbala, *etc.*)
Soloex nuestro deseo (Rhumbala, *etc.*)
Acabar con el fascismo (Rhumbala, *etc.*)
En el frente de Jarama (Rhumbala, *etc.*)
No tenemos ni aviones
Ni tankes, ni canones,
Ay Manuela, Ay Manuela.
Ya salimos de Espana (Rhumbala, *etc.*)
Por luchar en otras frentes (Rhumbala, *etc.*)

THE FOUR GENERALS
(Los Cuatro Generales)

*"Los Cuatro Generales"—Emilio Mola, José Varela, Gonzalo Queipo de Llano,
and Franco—converged on Madrid; a Spanish folk song about four muleteers
supplied the tune for the song that said in effect, "They shall not pass."*

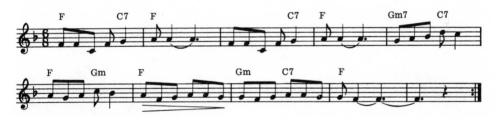

Four fascist rebel generals,
Four fascist rebel generals,
Four fascist rebel generals
Mamita mia,
They tried to betray us,
They tried to betray us.

By Christmas all these gen'rals
Mamita mia
Will dance on the gallows.

Bravely Madrid's resisting
Mamita mia
The fascist bombers.

We are laughing at the bombs,
Mamita mia
Madrid's proud children.

Los cuatro generales
Mamita mia
Que se han alzada.
Para la Nochebuena
Mamita mia
Serán ahorcados.
Madrid, qué bien resistes
Mamita mia
los bombardeos.
De las bombas se rien
Mamita mia
los Madrileños.

WALTZING MATILDA

*When it came, World War II would produce few songs of lasting consequence;
it wasn't a singing war. Of them all, the Australians, who brought their strange
and haunting ballad about Matilda, had the best. Americans who missed it heard
it later in the film* On the Beach.

Once a jolly swagman camped by a billabong
Under the shade of a coolibah tree,
And he sang as he watched and waited till his
    billy boiled,
"You'll come a-waltzing Matilda with me!"

Chorus:
Waltzing Matilda, Waltzing Matilda,
You'll come a-waltzing Matilda with me!
And he sang as he watched and waited till his
    billy boiled,
"You'll come a-waltzing Matilda with me!"

Down came a jumbuck to drink at the
    billabong,
Up jumped the swagman and grabbed him
    with glee,
And he sang as he stowed that jumbuck in his
    tucker bag.—*Cho.*

Up rode the squatter, mounted on his
    thoroughbred,
Down came the troopers, one, two, three,
"Where's that jolly jumbuck you've got in
    your tucker bag?"—*Cho.*

IN THAT CURSED MORNING OF HIROSHIMA
(Haru ni naru to)

*Written in 1966 by Tadashi Hidaka, here is a Japanese comment on the first use
of the A-bomb, twenty-one years earlier. Some Americans old enough to vote could
not remember it; others had forgotten, but Asia remembers. Published in* Broadside. *Used by permission.*

When peace came,
Those A-bombs and missiles
And cannons and tanks,
Swords and rifles,
Did we not vow
To throw them away?
But now, where has that vow gone?

Chorus:
How can we forget the flash!
How can we forget the mushroom cloud!
In that cursed morning of Hiroshima.

Haru ni naru to
Amai ka zega,
Akini naru to,
Tori no mure ga,
Yama no kanata e
Tonde itta no ni
Naze ima wa nai.
Ano senko ga
Wasure rare yoka!
Ano kinoko gumoga
Wasure rare yoka!
Hiroshima, no noroi no asa, no.

TO FREE OUR LAND
(Giai Phong Mien Nam)

Here, in words and music by Huynh Minh Sieng, is what the "other side" (the National Liberation Front of South Vietnam) is saying about the latest war. Published in Sing Out! *Used by permission.*

To free our land, determined, on we march,
Oppressed and tortured, hatred fills our
    hearts,
We'll build our ranks,
Rout the traitors and Yanks!
Imperialism's hour is come.
Our rivers and our mountains
The Mekong and Truong Son,
The long division of our land,
All spur us on to final victory:
Liberate our South Vietnam!
Heroic Southerners stand firm!
United we will brave the storm!
To save our land we'll fight to the end.
March onward, guns in hand.
Our day is nigh,
Bright dawn fills the sky,
A shining future for our land!

Giai phong Mien Nam, chungta cung quyet
    tion buoc
Diet de quoc
My pha tan be lu ban nuoc
Oi zuong tan mau roi long han thu ngain tro
Song nui bao nhieu nam cat roi
Day Cuu long hungtrang
Day Truong son vinh quang
Thuc guic doan ta xung phong o giet
Thu vai sat vai chung mot bong ca.

Refrain:
Vung len nhan dan Mien Nam anh hung
Vung len xong pha vuot qua hao bung
The cuu lay nuoc nha.
The hy sinh den cung cam quom om sung
    xong toi
Van nuoc da toi roi hinh minh chieu khap noi
Nguyen xov non nuoc sang tuoi muon doi.

THE WILLING CONSCRIPT
(I've Never Killed Before)

Tom Paxton wrote the words and music for this song back in 1963, before many draftees had developed strong resistance. Its satire belongs to any war in which young men agree to fight for causes they fail to understand. Copyright 1963 by Cherry Lane Music, Inc. All rights reserved. Used by permission.

Oh, Sergeant, I'm a draftee, and I've just arrived in camp,
I've come to wear the uniform and join the martial tramp,
And I want to do my duty, but one thing I do implore,
You must give me lessons, Sergeant,
For I've never killed before.

To do my job obediently is my only desire,
To learn my weapon thoroughly and how to aim and fire,
To learn to kill the enemy and then to slaughter more,
I'll need instructions, Sergeant,
For I've never killed before.

Now, there are rumors in the camp about our enemy;
They say that when you see him he looks just like you and me;
But you deny it, Sergeant, and you are a man of war,
So you must give me lessons,
For I've never killed before.

Now, there are several lessons that I haven't mastered yet,
I haven't got the hang of how to use the bayonet;
If he doesn't die at once, am I to stick him with it more?
Oh, I hope you will be patient,
For I've never killed before.

And the hand grenade is something that I just don't understand,
You've got to throw it quickly or you're apt to lose your hand;
Does it blow a man to pieces with its wicked, muffled roar?
Oh, I've got so much to learn because I've never killed before.

Well, I want to thank you, Sergeant, for the help you've been to me,
You've taught me how to kill, and how to hate the enemy,
And I know that I'll be ready when they march me off to war.
And I know that it won't matter that I've never killed before;
I know that it won't matter that I've never killed before.

I WANT TO GO TO ANDORRA!

The unwilling taxpayer for war is given a suggestion in this lyric by Val Shannon, with a tune by Pete Seeger. Copyright 1962 by Val Shannon and Pete Seeger; first published in Broadside. *Used by permission.*

In the mountains of the Pyrenees there's an independent state.
Its population five thousand souls and I think they're simply great.
One hundred and seventy square miles big, and it's mighty plain to see:
Spends less'n five dollars on armaments, and this I've got to see!

Chorus:
I want to go to Andorra, Andorra, Andorra!
I want to go to Andorra, it's a land that I adore.
They spent four dollars and ninety cents
On armaments and their defense;
Did you ever hear o' such confidence?
Andorra, hip hoorah!

It's governed by a council, all gentle souls and wise,
Spent only five dollars on armaments, and the rest on cakes and pies.
They didn't invest in a tommygun or a plane to sweep the sky,
But they bought some blanks for cap pistols to shoot on their 4th of July!—*Cho.*

They live by the arts of farm and field, and by making shoes and hats;
They haven't got room in their tiny land for a horde of diplomats;
They haven't got room in their tiny land for armies to march about;
And if anyone comes with a war budget, they throw the rascals out.—*Cho.*

There are no superhighways there, for where would the highways go?
They just slide down the Pyrenees whenever it starts to snow;
And when the springtime comes around, they love to sing and play,
And if anyone comes with a war budget, they holler, "Go away!"—*Cho.*

IV

WORK SONGS

The work of men's hands, though lacking a mechanical beat, has always moved to its own rhythms. From the "Gung Ho" of Chinese dam builders carrying earth in baskets to the shout of John Henry in desperate competition with the steam drill, workers' songs began by expressing the physical movements of their world—tugging at ropes, picking cotton, loading cargo, drilling rock, or herding cattle. That hard physical labor goes best to music means that seamen, field hands, roustabouts, drillers, and cowboys, with their own labor values for the world, are all well represented in song.

So, too, songs helped the machine-age worker who learned a different kind of coordination and cooperation, that of the unions whose establishment brought changed conditions in work and pay. Good union songs resemble war songs and college songs in that their function is to furnish inspiration for united effort. Their range is wide, their style varied, and although they belong to the earlier stages of union organization rather than to the era of sophisticated bargaining, they have done much for American labor. In the early days some, like other work songs, were folk songs of unrecorded origin; others have made famous the name of Woody Guthrie or of Earl Robinson, composer of "Ballad for Americans" and of the haunting song about Joe Hill, who wrote songs himself. Written before *The Grapes of Wrath*, Joe Hill's requiem must have been the inspiration for Tom Joad's famous farewell to his mother: "I'll be everywhere—everywhere you look. Wherever there's a fight so hungry people can eat, I'll be there. Wherever there's a cop beatin' up a guy, I'll be there. . . ." Woody Guthrie's song "Tom Joad" restates the idea for the third time, and thus Joe Hill does live on.

YOU GENTLEMEN OF ENGLAND

This early ballad, date and origin unrecorded, puts the case for the hard-working British seaman versus the idle rich, and, like all sea songs, it has a moving rhythm.

You gentlemen of England who live at home at ease,
How little do you think upon the dangers of the seas.
Give ear unto the mariners, and they will plainly show
All the cares, and the fears, when the stormy winds do blow.
All the cares, and the fears,
When the stormy winds do blow.

All you that will be seamen must bear a valiant heart,
For when you come upon the sea you must not think to start.
Nor once to be fainthearted, in rain, hail, blow or snow,
Nor to think for to shrink when the stormy winds do blow.
Nor to think for to shrink when the stormy winds do blow.

The lawyer and the usurer, that sit in gowns of fur
In closets warm can take no harm, abroad they need not stir.
When winter fierce with cold doth pierce, and beats with hail and snow,
We are sure to endure when the stormy winds do blow.
We are sure to endure
When the stormy winds do blow.

Then courage, all brave mariners, and never be dismayed;
Whilst we have bold adventurers we ne'er shall want a trade.
Our merchants will employ us to fetch them wealth, I know,
Then behold, work for gold, when the stormy winds do blow.
Then behold, work for gold,
When the stormy winds do blow.

BLOW THE MAN DOWN

Described as a "hoisting chantey," this one from the days of sail began in England and suffered a sea change between Limehouse and Newport. Here is the English version.

As I was a-walkin' down Paradise Street
(Way! Hey!—blow the man down!)
A saucy young p'liceman I chanced for to meet;
Blow the man down to me aye, aye, blow the man down!
Whether he's white man or black man or brown,
Give me some time to blow the man down,
Give me some time to blow the man down,
Blow the man down! bullies!

You're off from some clipper that flies the Black Ball,
(Way! Hey!—blow the man down!)

You've robbed some poor Dutchman of coat, boots, and all;
Blow the man down, etc.

P'liceman, p'liceman, you do me much wrong
(Way! Hey!—blow the man down!)
I'm a peace party sailor just home from Hong Kong;
Blow the man down, etc.

They gave me six months in Ledington jail
(Way! Hey!—blow the man down!)
For kickin' and fightin' and knockin' 'em down;
Blow the man down, etc.

BLOW, BOYS, BLOW

Instead of romance or a jail term, this song is concerned with rations—always important to men long at sea.

Solo:
Blow, my bullies, I long to hear you!
Blow, my bullies, I come to cheer you!

Chorus:
Blow, boys, blow! my bully
Blow, boys, blow!

A Yankee ship's gone down the river
And what do you think they got for dinner?
—*Cho.*

Dandy funk and donkey's liver
Then blow, my boys, for better weather.—*Cho.*

THE MERMAID

Landlubbers may not know that mermaids are bad luck, but sailors are better informed. No one now knows the author or authors of this song, but the swinging chorus can still inspire even landlubbers doing a mile around the shining deck of a cruise liner.

'Twas Friday morn when we set sail,
And we were not far from the land
When the captain spied a lovely mermaid
With a comb and a glass in her hand.

Chorus:
Oh, the ocean waves may roll,
And the stormy winds may blow,
While we poor sailors go skipping to the tops,
And the landlubbers lie down below,
   below, below,
And the landlubbers lie down below.

Then up spake the captain of our gallant ship,
And a well-spoken man was he;

"I have married a wife in Salem town,
And tonight she a widow will be."—*Cho.*

Then up spake the cook of our gallant ship,
And a red-hot cook was he;
"I care much more for my kettles and my pots,
Than I do for the depths of the sea."—*Cho.*

Then three times around went our gallant
   ship,
And three times around went she,
Then three times around went our gallant
   ship,
And she sank to the depths of the sea.—*Cho.*

SHENANDOAH

Rivermen sang also, and Mark Twain argued that the Missouri was a better river than the Mississippi. Composer and lyricist are unknown, but the period would be the early 1800's.

Leader:
Oh, Shenandoah, I long to hear you

Chorus:
Away, you rolling river

Leader:
Oh, Shenandoah, I long to hear you

Chorus:
Away, we're bound away,
'Cross the wide Missouri.

Missouri she's a mighty river,
The Indians camp along its borders.

The white man loved an Indian maiden,
With notions his canoe was laden.

Oh, Shenandoah, I love your daughter,
I've crossed for her the rolling water.

The chief, he made an awful holler,
He turned away the trader's dollars.

Along there came a Yankee skipper,
He winked at her and tipped his flipper.

He sold the chief some fire water,
He got him drunk and stole his daughter.

Fare you well, I'm bound to leave you,
Oh, Shenandoah, I'll not deceive you.

ERIE CANAL

The man-made waterway connecting the Great Lakes with the Atlantic had its own songs. Here is a relic of the days when mulepower moved the barges.

I've got a mule, her name is Sal,
Fifteen miles on the Erie Canal.
She's a good old worker and a good old pal,
Fifteen miles on the Erie Canal.
We've hauled some barges in our day,
Filled with lumber, coal, and hay,
And we know every inch of the way
From Albany to Buffalo.

Chorus:
Low bridge, everybody down!
Low bridge, for we're going through a town;

And you'll always know your neighbor, you'll
 always know your pal,
If you ever navigated on the Erie Canal.

Git up there, Sal, we passed a lock,
Fifteen miles on the Erie Canal,
And we'll make Rome 'fore six o'clock,
Fifteen miles on the Erie Canal.
Just one more trip and back we'll go
Through the rain and sleet and snow,
'Cause we know every inch of the way
From Albany to Buffalo.

STEAMBOAT BILL

Captain Bill's Mississippi steamboat had power, but there were hazards, and the accident rate in the days of steamboat racing made it a dangerous mode of travel. Words by Ben Shields; music by Leighton Brothers.

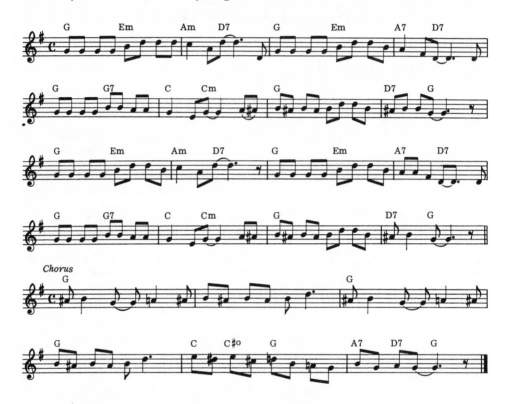

Down the Mississippi steamed the *Whipperwill*
Commanded by that pilot, Mister Steamboat Bill.
The owners gave him orders on the strict q.t.
To try and beat the record of the *Robert E. Lee.*

"Just feed up your fires, let the old smoke roll,
Burn up your cargo if you run out of coal."
"If we don't beat that record," Billy told the mate,
"Send my mail in care of Peter to the Golden Gate."

Chorus:
Steamboat Bill, steaming down the Mississippi,
Steamboat Bill, a mighty man was he.
Steamboat Bill, steaming down the Mississippi,
Going to beat the record of the *Robert E. Lee.*

Up then stepped a gambling man from Louisville,
Who tried to get a bet against the *Whipperwill.*
Billy flashed a roll that surely was a bear;
The boiler it exploded, blew them up in the air.

The gambler said to Billy as they left the wreck,
"I don't know where we're going but we're neck 'n' neck."
Says Billy to the gambler, "I'll tell you what I'll do;
I will bet another thousand I'll go higher than you."

Chorus:
Steamboat Bill, he tore up the Mississippi,
Steamboat Bill, the tide it made him swear.
Steamboat Bill, he tore up the Mississippi,
The explosion of the boiler got him up in the air.

River's all in mourning now for Steamboat Bill,
No more you'll hear the puffing of the *Whipperwill*.
There's crepe on every steamboat that plows those streams
From Memphis right to Natchez down to New Orleans.

The wife of Mister William was at home in bed,
When she got the telegram that Steamboat's dead.
Says she to the children, "Bless each honey lamb,
The next papa that you have will be a railroad man."

Chorus:
Steamboat Bill, missing on the Mississippi,
Steamboat Bill, is with an angel band.
Steamboat Bill, missing on the Mississippi,
He's a pilot on a ferry in that Promised Land.

VOLGA BOAT SONG

On the Russian towpath, in the old days, manpower pulled instead of mules; so this Russian song, like those of sail, helped men on the long haul. Its date of composition is unknown; it was popular until 1917.

Yo heave ho! Yo heave ho! Where the Volga's waters flow.
Yo heave ho! Yo heave ho! Brave men plodding, strong and slow.
"Onward, brothers, on!" they cry,
"Toward the birch that lines the sky."
Taut to their singing, towlines are swinging,
Where the Volga's waters flow.

Yo heave ho! Yo heave ho! Where the Volga's waters flow.
Yo heave ho! Yo heave ho! See them toiling, strong and slow.
Toward the birch tree, till the plain.
Toil was never done in vain.
Endless their singing, birch cables swinging,
Chanting from our sight they go.

LEVEE SONG

Long before Old Man River, they were rolling down the bales; in this one, river and railroad freight made a dual burden, leading logically to the next song.

Oh, I was bo'n in Mobile town, A wuk-kin on de levee,
All day I roll de cotton down, A wuk-kin on de levee.
I use' to have a dawg name' Bill, A wuk-kin on de levee,
He run away but I'm here still, A wuk-kin on de levee.

LEVEE MOAN

*The Ohio River, as well as the Mississippi, according to Carl Sandburg, knew this
one; that explains the complaint about the climate. A similar shivery moan
occurs in other songs sung by workers going north.*

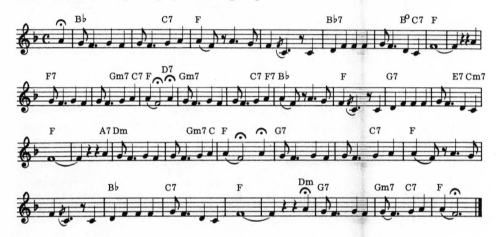

Ah'm goin' whah nobody knows mah name,
Lawd, Lawd, Lawd, Lawd!
Ah'm goin' whah nobody knows mah name!
Ah'm goin' whah nobody knows mah name!

Ah'm goin' whah dey don't shovel no snow,
Lawd, Lawd, Lawd, Lawd!

Ah'm goin' whah dey don't shovel no snow!
Ah'm goin' whah dey don't shovel no snow!

Ah'm goin' whah de chilly wind don't blow,
Lawd, Lawd, Lawd, Lawd!
Ah'm doin' whah de chilly wind don't blow!
Ah'm doin' whah de chilly wind don't blow!

DRILL, YE TARRIERS, DRILL

*When railroads took over the river traffic, it meant blasting rock to lay tracks,
and dynamite blasts became a work hazard. Irish workers did the job, as this
famous old song with music by Charles Connolly indicates.*

Every morning at seven o'clock
There were twenty tarriers a-working on the rock,
And the boss comes along, and he says, "Kape still,
And come down heavy on the cast iron drill."

Chorus:
And drill, ye tarriers, drill! Drill, ye tarriers, drill!
And you work all day for the sugar in your tay, down behind the railway,
And drill, ye tarriers, drill, and blast, and fire!

The boss was a fine man to the ground,
And he married a lady six feet round.
She baked good bread and she baked it well,
But she baked it hard as the holes in hell.—*Cho.*

The new foreman was Jean McCann,
By God, he was a blame mean man.
Last week a premature blast went off,
And a mile in the air went big Jim Goff.—*Cho.*

When the next payday came around,
Jim Goff a dollar short was found.
When he asked, "What for?" came this reply,
"You're docked for the time you was up in the sky."—*Cho.*

I'VE BEEN WUKKIN' ON THE RAILROAD

This classic of the age of mechanization spread over the country almost as fast, in the early 1800's, as the ribbons of steel that spanned the miles. The tune, also used with "The Eyes of Texas," is an old hymn.

Wuk, wuk, wuk, wuk, wuk, wuk . . .
I've been wukkin' on the railroad,
All the livelong day.
I've been wukkin' on the railroad
Just to pass the time away.

Doan' you heah the whistle blowin',
Rise up so early in the mawn;
Doan' you heah the cap'n shoutin',
"Dinah, blow you' hawn!"

JOHN HENRY

When John Henry undertook to beat the steam drill, the Negro in a southern work camp became the symbol of man against machine. There are many versions of this song, a saga in itself. In his Songbag, *Carl Sandburg tells the tale.*

John Henry tol' his cap'n
Dat a man wuz a natural man,
An' befo' he'd let dat steam drill run him
  down,
He'd fall dead wid a hammer in his han',
He'd fall dead wid a hammer in his han'.

Cap'n he sez to John Henry:
"Gonna bring me a steam drill 'round;
Take that steel drill out on the job,
Gonna whop that steel on down,
Gonna whop that steel on down."

John Henry sez to his cap'n:
"Send me a twelve-poun' hammer aroun',
A twelve-poun' hammer wid a fo'-foot handle,

An' I beat yo' steam drill down,
An' I beat yo' steam drill down."

John Henry went down de railroad
Wid a twelve-poun' hammer by his side,
He walked down de track but he didn't come
  back,
'Cause he laid down his hammer an' he died,
'Cause he laid down his hammer an' he died.

John Henry had a li'l' ooman,
Her name wuz Polly Ann.
On de day John Henry he drap daid
Polly Ann hammered steel like a man,
Polly Ann hammered steel like a man.

PICK A BALE A DAY

To pick a bale of cotton a day you had to be good. Now the machine does it faster, and what the Rust brothers, its inventors, meant to be a trouble-saver makes trouble for southern field hands. Made jobless, they move north to the cities that are unprepared to offer a welcome.

You got to jump down, turn around,
Pick a bale o' cotton,
Got to jump down, turn around,
Pick a bale a day.

Oh, Lawdy,
Pick a bale o' cotton,
Oh, Lawdy,
Pick a bale a day.

Me and my pardner can
Pick a bale o' cotton,
Me and my pardner can
Pick a bale a day.

(similarly:)
Me and my wife can—

Me and my brother can—

Me and my papa can—

Had a little woman could—

I b'lieve to my soul I can—

Went to Corsicana to—

WEAVE-ROOM BLUES

After cotton got to the mill for weaving, it still meant hard work, and changing to rayon didn't help. "Fighting for my life" in a southern textile mill meant not only starvation-level wages but also disease caused by breathing in lint for a ten-hour day, at the time songs of mill life began. Words and music of this one by Dorothy Dixon. Used by permission.

Workin' in a weave-room, fightin' for my life,
Tryin' to make a livin' for my kiddies and my wife,
Some are needin' clothin' and some are needin' shoes,
But I'm gettin' nothin' but them weave-room blues.

Chorus: I got the blues, I got the blues,
  I got them awful weave-room blues;
  I got the blues, the weave-room blues.

With your looms a-slammin', shuttles bouncin' on the floor,
And when you flag your fixer, you can see that he is sore.
I'm tryin' to make a livin' but I'm thinkin' I will lose,
For I'm a-gettin' nothin' but them weave-room blues.—*Cho.*

COTTON MILL GIRLS

This song has many variants in the southern mill country, with no one to claim authorship. The last verse given here is usually sung by men; some girls drink, but more chew gum or dip snuff. Published in Sing Out! *Used by permission.*

I worked in the cotton mill all of my life,
And I ain't got nothin' but a Barlow knife.
It's a hard time, cotton mill girls,
It's a hard time everywhere. *(three times)*

When I die, don't bury me at all,
Just hang me up on the spinning room wall,
Pickle my bones in alcohol.
It's a hard time everywhere.

POOR MINER'S FAREWELL

Mine disasters still make news, and modern folk songs, like the old ones, tell sad stories. A famous maker of songs, Aunt Molly Jackson, wrote this one.

They leave their dear wives, and little ones too,
To earn them a living, as miners all do.
Poor hardworking miners, their troubles are great—
So often, while mining, they meet their sad fate.

Chorus:
Only a miner killed under the ground,
Only a miner and one more is found,
Killed by some accident, there's no one can tell—
Your mining's all over, poor miner, farewell.

Poor orphaned children, thrown out on the street,
Ragged and hungry with nothing to eat.
Their mothers are jobless and their fathers are dead;
Poor fatherless children, left a-crying for bread.—*Cho.*

When I'm in Kentucky so often I meet
Poor coal miner's children out on the street,
"How are you doing?" to them I said,
"We're hungry, Aunt Molly; we're begging for bread."—*Cho.*

WHICH SIDE ARE YOU ON?

An old union song with words by Florence Reece is sung to an older hymn tune. Like Aunt Molly Jackson, Mrs. Reece, a miner's widow, lives in the Kentucky coalfields.

Come all of you good workers, news to you I'll tell
Of how the good old union has come in here to dwell.

Refrain:
Which side are you on?

Which side are you on?
Which side are you on?
Which side are you on?

They say in Harlan County, there are no neutrals there.
You'll either be a union man, or a thug for J. H. Blair.—*Ref.*

Oh, workers, can you stand it? Oh, tell me how you can.
Will you be a lousy scab, or will you be a man?—*Ref.*

Don't scab for the bosses, don't listen to their lies.
Us poor folks haven't got a chance, unless we organize.—*Ref.*

My daddy was a miner, and I'm a miner's son,
And I'll stick with the union, till every battle's won.—*Ref.*

UNION MAID

During an early mill strike, Woody Guthrie wrote this one to the popular old tune "Red Wing." The strike occurred in what had been Indian territory; "my pretty Red Wing" was an Indian girl. Copyright 1961, 1963 by Ludlow Music, Inc., New York. All rights reserved. Used by permission.

There once was a union maid,
She never was afraid
Of goons and ginks and company finks
And deputy sheriffs that made the raids.
She went to the union hall
When a meeting it was called,
And when the comp'ny boys came 'round
She always stood her ground.

Chorus:
Oh, you can't scare me,
I'm sticking to the union,
I'm sticking to the union,
I'm sticking to the union.
Oh, you can't scare me,
I'm sticking to the union,
I'm sticking to the union,
'Til the day I die.

This union maid was wise
To the tricks of company spies;
She couldn't be fooled by a company stool,
She'd always organize the guys.
She'd always get her way
When she asked for better pay;
She'd show her card to the company guard,
And this is what she'd say:—*Cho.*

Now, you gals who want to be free,
Just take a little tip from me;
Get you a man who's a union man,
And fight together for liberty;
Married life ain't hard
When you got a union card,
And a union man leads a happy life
When he's got a union wife.—*Cho.*

GUNG HO!

Chinese workers repeat the "work together" slogan in this one, sung to an ancient tune of the chantey type.

Come fellow workers, gung ho hai ho,
Seek emancipation, gung ho hai ho.
Ho, ho, ho tsili gung ho,
Ho, ho, gung-yo-lo-yo hai.

Come fellow workers, gung ho hai ho,
Fight for freedom, gung ho hai ho.
Ho, ho, ho tsili gung ho,
Ho, ho, gung-yo-lo-yo hai.

GIT ALONG, LITTLE DOGIES

Workers who went west for ranch jobs often found that a cowboy's life had its own hardships. Easterners should remember that "dogies" are not "doggies." As with genuine cowboy songs, this one lacks a traceable origin.

As I was a-walking one morning for pleasure,
I spied a cowpuncher come riding along;
His hat was throwed back, and his spurs was a-jingling,
And as he approached, he was singing this song.

Chorus:
Whoopee ti yi yo, git along, little dogies,
It's your misfortune and none of my own;
Whoopee ti yi yo, git along, little dogies,
You know that Wyoming will be your new home.

It's early in spring that we round up the dogies,
And mark 'em and brand 'em and bob off their tails;
We round up our horses and load the chuck wagon,
And then throw the dogies out onto the trail.—*Cho.*

It's whoopin' and yellin' and a-drivin' them dogies,
Oh, how I wish that you would go on;
It's a-whoopin' and punchin' and go on-a, little dogies,
For you know Wyoming is to be your new home.—*Cho.*

Some cowboys go up the trail just for pleasure,
But that's where they get it most awfully wrong,
For nobody knows what trouble they give us,
As we go driving them all along.—*Cho.*

THE OLD CHISHOLM TRAIL

Even the "best durn cowboy" had to get up early, work in the rain, and got tired of eating beans. As the last verses show, he may resolve to quit, but he has to eat. Tune and verses are traditional, of the days when the trail was used.

I woke up one morning on the old Chisholm trail,
Rope in my hand and a cow by the tail,

Two-dollar horse and a forty-dollar saddle,
I could see I was ready to go punch cattle.

I jumped in the saddle and grabbed the horn,
Best durn cowboy that ever was born.

Up in the morning before daylight,
And before I sleep the moon shines bright.

Oh, it's bacon and beans most every day,
I'd just as soon eat a pile of prairie hay.

It's cloudy in the west and it looks like rain,
And my damned old slicker's in the wagon again.

It's raining like hell and it's getting mighty cold,
And these long-horned so-and-sos are gettin' hard to hold.

I herded and I hollered and I done right well,
Till the boss he says just to let 'em go to hell.

So, I went to the boss to draw my roll,
He figured me out nine dollars in the hole.

I didn't like that so we had a little chat;
I slapped him in the face with my big slouch hat.

So I sold my rope and I sold my saddle,
'Cause I'm gettin' tired of punchin' these goddam cattle.

Goin' back to town to draw my money,
Goin' back home to see my honey.

I'll ride my horse to the top of the hill,
I'll kiss my gal, goldurn, I will.

My seat is in the saddle, and my saddle's in the sky;
And I'll quit punchin' cows in the sweet by and by.

SIT DOWN

When mechanization went merrily on, with inadequate returns for the workers, from Cleveland, Ohio, to Flint, Michigan, they tried just sitting. Maurice Sugar wrote this song.

When they try to can a union man, sit down, sit down;
If they give him the sack, they'll take him back; sit down, sit down.

Chorus:
Sit down, just take a seat;
Sit down and rest your feet.
Sit down, you've got 'em beat;
Sit down!
Sit down!

When they smile and say, "No raise in pay," sit down, sit down.
When you want the boss to come across, sit down, sit down.—*Cho.*

When the speed-up comes, just twiddle your thumbs, sit down, sit down.
When you want 'em to know they'd better go slow, sit down, sit down.—*Cho.*

When the boss won't talk, don't take a walk; sit down, sit down.
When the boss sees that, he'll want a little chat; sit down, sit down.—*Cho.*

WE SHALL NOT BE MOVED
(Fuertes Somos Ya)

For farm workers the problem was different; in the thirties, Arkansas sharecroppers talking union were moved out of their shacks. Camped along the highway, they sang this song, with its origin in the first of the Psalms. Now braceros in California sing a Spanish version.

We're fighting for our freedom, we shall not be moved;
We're fighting for our freedom, we shall not be moved.
Just like a tree that's standing by the water,
We shall not be moved.

Fuertes, fuertes, fuertes somos ya;
Fuertes, fuertes, fuertes somos ya
Como un árbol juntos cerca al río,
Fuertes somos ya.

Queremos mejor sueldo, fuertes somos ya;
Queremos mejor sueldo, fuertes somos ya
Como un árbol juntos cerca al río,
Fuertes somos ya.

Abajo con la guerra, fuertes somos ya;
Abajo con la guerra, fuertes somos ya
Como un árbol juntos cerca al río,
Fuertes somos ya.

Unidos venceremos, fuertes somos ya;
Unidos venceremos, fuertes somos ya
Como un árbol juntos cerca al río,
Fuertes somos ya.

Patria o muerte, fuertes somos ya;
Patria o muerte, fuertes somos ya
Como un árbol juntos cerca al río,
Fuertes somos ya.

SOLIDARITY FOREVER
(Solidaridad para Siempre)

An old favorite among union songs is this one by Ralph Chaplin, sung to one of the many adaptations of "John Brown's Body." Now there is also a Spanish version, sung in the Southwest.

When the union's inspiration through a worker's blood shall run,
There can be no power greater anywhere beneath the sun.
Yet what force on earth is weaker than the feeble strength of one?
It's the union makes us strong.

Chorus: Solidarity forever, solidarity forever.
Solidarity forever, for the union makes us strong.

En las viñas de la íra luchan por su libertad
Todos los trabajadores quieren ya vivir en paz
Y por eso campañeros nos tenemos que juntar
Con solidaridad. *(Ahora Todos!)*

Solidaridad pa' siempre,
Solidaridad pa' siempre,
Solidaridad pa' siempre,
¡Que viva nuestra Unión!

BRACERO

Latin workers along the Rio Grande and the Lower California border, in the "factories in the fields" for vegetables and in the orchards and vineyards, are now asking for better working conditions and a living wage. Words and music by Phil Ochs, copyright 1965 by Barricade Music, Inc. All rights reserved. Used by permission.

Wade into the river through the rippling shadow waters,
Steal across the thirsty border, Bracero;
Come bring your hungry body to the golden fields of plenty,
Sell your soul for half a penny, Bracero.

Chorus:
And welcome to California,
Where the friendly farmers will take care of you.

Come labor for your mother, for your father and your brothers,
For your sisters and your lover, Bracero;
Come pick the fruits of yellow, break the flowers from the berries,
Purple grapes will fill your belly, Bracero.—*Cho.*

The sun will bite your body as the dust will dry you thirsty,
While your muscles beg for mercy, Bracero.
Oh, your bones are slowly curving, bending lower than the soil;
Like the fruit, your youth can spoil, Bracero.—*Cho.*

When the weary night embraces sleep in shacks that could be cages,
They will take it from your wages, Bracero.
Come sing about tomorrow with the jingle of the dollars
And forget your slavery collars, Bracero.—*Cho.*

The local men are lazy and they make too much of trouble,
'Sides we'd have to pay them double, Bracero.
Ah, but if you feel you're falling, if you find the pace is killing,
There are others who are willing, Bracero.—*Cho.*

EV'RYBODY LOVES SATURDAY NIGHT

No wageworker needs to know why this song, originating in West Africa as a protest against a British curfew, spread around the world. Schoolchildren in California made a project of finding different language versions, with French, English, Yiddish, Chinese, Russian, Japanese, and Czech, as well as the original Nigerian, all represented.

Ev'rybody loves Saturday night,
Ev'rybody loves Saturday night,
Ev'rybody, ev'rybody, ev'rybody, ev'rybody,
Ev'rybody loves Saturday night.

French:
Tout le monde aime samedi soir,
Tout le monde, tout le monde,
Tout le monde, tout le monde,
Tout le monde aime samedi soir.

Yiddish:
Jeder eyne hot lieb Shabas ba nacht,
Jeder eyne hot, jeder eyne hot,
Jeder eyne hot, jeder eyne hot,
Jeder eyne hot lieb Shabas ba nacht.

German:
Jedermann hat dem Samstag Abend,
Jedermann hat dem Samstag Abend,
Jedermann hat, Jedermann hat, Jedermann
    hat, Jedermann hat,
Jedermann hat dem Samstag Abend.

Spanish:
El Sábado ama todo el mundo,
El Sábado ama todo el mundo,
Todo el mundo, todo el mundo, todo el
    mundo, todo el mundo,
El Sábado ama todo el mundo.

Norwegian:
Alle elsker Lordag kveld,
Alle elsker Lordag kveld,
Alle elsker, alle elsker, alle elsker,
    alle elsker,
Alle elsker Lordag kveld.

Danish:
Alle elsker Lordag aften,
Alle elsker Lordag aften,
Alle elsker, alle elsker, alle elsker,
    alle elsker,
Alle elsker Lordag aften.

JOE HILL

Here is the "spiritual" of the union movement, with words by Alfred Hayes and music by Earl Robinson. © 1938 by MCA Music, a division of MCA Inc., New York, N.Y. All rights reserved. Used by permission.

I dreamed I saw Joe Hill last night
Alive as you and me;
Says I, "But Joe, you're ten years dead."
"I never died," says he.
"I never died," says he.

"In Salt Lake, Joe, by God," says I,
Him standing by my bed,
"They framed you on a murder charge."
Says Joe, "But I ain't dead."
Says Joe, "But I ain't dead."

"The copper bosses killed you, Joe.
They shot you, Joe," says I.
"Takes more than guns to kill a man,"
Says Joe, "I didn't die."
Says Joe, "I didn't die."

And standing there as big as life,
And smiling with his eyes,
Joe says, "What they forgot to kill

Went on to organize,
Went on to organize."

"Joe Hill ain't dead," he says to me.
"Joe Hill ain't never died.
Where workingmen are out on strike
Joe Hill is at their side,
Joe Hill is at their side."

"From San Diego up to Maine
In every mine and mill,
Where workers strike and organize,"
Says he, "You find Joe Hill."
Says he, "You find Joe Hill."

I dreamed I saw Joe Hill last night
Alive as you and me.
Says I, "But Joe, you're ten years dead."
"I never died," says he.
"I never died," says he.

V

SONGS OF HARD TIMES

There are Americans who remember the Great Depression of the thirties with a horror beyond that felt for the world wars. For prevention of both, the new songmakers are doing their best, and a part of their task is to convey the feeling of dark days already experienced in a manner to move those lacking the experience. Recollections are varied; economic causes are worldwide; but people already hard up in better times were hit even harder in the hungry thirties. Negroes, farmers, and mill hands did not jump from high windows as did the stock gamblers; instead they moved on over dusty roads, on foot or in battered jalopies, as the songs of those days reveal.

In the depressed thirties a young man sat in a dark theatre and laughed as Walt Disney's plump little pigs sang their brave defiance of fortune, to a tune that reminded some people of another happy nursery rhyme, "Santa Claus Will Come Tonight." Within ten years that same young man would be earning fifty thousand a year, but at the time he was hungry, and unaware that a temporary twenty-a-week job was just around the corner. He *was* afraid of the Big Bad Wolf, but he took courage from the Three Little Pigs—as others in various degrees of anxiety have been cheered by the appropriate tune. Yes, the sad or tough songs help too.

NOBODY KNOWS THE TROUBLE I'VE SEEN

This old song is not one of temporary hard times, as the white folks know them; it states, mildly, a more or less permanent condition of Negroes in the South, to whom a "depression" was no news.

Oh, nobody knows the trouble I've seen,
Nobody knows but Jesus!
Nobody knows, the trouble I've seen,
Glory, hallelujah!

Sometimes I'm up, sometimes I'm down,
Oh, yes, Lord.
Sometimes I'm almost to the ground,
Oh, yes, Lord.

MY OKLAHOMA HOME, IT BLOWED AWAY

In the cities factories closed down, while in the dustbowl farms literally went with the wind. This song, by Bill and Sis Cunningham, whose father was a homesteader in Oklahoma, tells the story. Copyright 1961, 1962 by Fall River Music, Inc. All rights reserved. Used by permission.

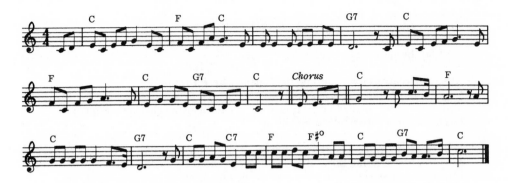

When they opened up the strip I was young and full of zip,
I wanted a place to call my own.
And so I made the race, and staked me out a place,
And settled down along the Cimarron.

Chorus:
It blowed away, it blowed away,
My Oklahoma home, it blowed away.
It looked so green and fair when I built my shanty there,
But my Oklahoma home, it blowed away.

I planted wheat and oats, got some chickens and some shoats,
Aimed to have some ham and eggs to feed my face.
Got a mule to pull the plow, got an old red muley cow
And got a fancy mortgage on the place.

It blowed away, it blowed away,
All the crops I planted blowed away.
You can't grow any grain if there isn't any rain;
All except the mortgage blowed away.

It blowed away my rooster and it blowed away my hens;
The pigs and cattle went astray.
All the crops that I sowed went a-foggin' down the road.
My Oklahoma farm, it blowed away.

It blowed away, it blowed away,
Everything I owned blowed away.
I hollered and I cussed when my land went up in dust,
When my Oklahoma farm, it blowed away.

It looked so green and fair, when I built my shanty there,
I figured I was all set for life.
I put on my Sunday best with my fancy scalloped vest
And went to town and picked me out a wife.

She blowed away, she blowed away,
My Oklahoma woman blowed away.
Just as I bent and kissed her, she was picked up by a twister;
My Oklahoma woman blowed away.

Then I was left alone a-listenin' to the moan
Of the wind around the corners of my shack;
So I took off down the road when the south wind blowed,
A-travelin' with the wind at my back.

I blowed away, I blowed away
Chasin' a dust cloud up ahead.
Once it looked so green and fair, now it's up there in the air;
My Oklahoma farm is overhead.

Now I'm always close to home no matter where I roam,
For Oklahoma dust is everywhere.
Makes no difference where I'm walkin', I can hear my chickens squawkin',
I can hear my wife a-talkin' in the air.

It blowed away, it blowed away,
My Oklahoma home blowed away.
But my home is always near; it's in the atmosphere,
My Oklahoma home that blowed away.

I'm a roamin' Oklahoman, but I'm always close to home
And I'll never get homesick 'til I die.
No matter where I'm found, my home is all around;
My Oklahoma home is in the sky.

It blowed away, it blowed away,
My farm down upon the Cimarron.
But all around the world, wherever dust is whirled,
Some is from my Oklahoma home.

Spare Tire Chorus:
It blowed away, it blowed away,
My Oklahoma home blowed away.
Oh, it's up there in the sky in that dust cloud rolling by,
My Oklahoma home is in the sky.

THERE IS MEAN THINGS HAPPENING IN THIS LAND

In Arkansas, dispossessed sharecroppers bore the brunt of the hard times. John Handcox, an organizer for the union, wrote the song that tells of their plight. With later verses by Chick and Sis Cunningham, published in Hard Hitting Songs for Hard Hit People, *copyright 1967 by Oak Publishing Co. All rights reserved. Used by permission.*

There is mean things happening in this land,
There is mean things happening in this land.
But the union's going on,
And the union's going strong.
There is mean things happening in this land.

The planters throwed the people off the land,
Where many years they'd spent,
And in the hard cold winter,
They had to live in tents.

The planters throwed the people out,
Without a bite to eat,
They cursed them and kicked them,
And some with axe handles beat.

The people got tired of working for nothing,
And that from sun to sun,
But the planters forced some to work
At the point of guns.

There is mean things happening in this land. *(Repeat.)*
Oh, the rich man boasts and brags while the poor man goes in rags,
There is mean things happening in this land.

There is mean things happening in this land. *(Repeat.)*
Oh, the farmer cannot eat, 'cause he's raised too much wheat,
There is mean things happening in this land.

There is mean things happening in this land. *(Repeat.)*
Too much cotton in our sacks so we have none on our backs,
There is mean things happening in this land.

There is mean things happening in this land. *(Repeat.)*
Lots of groceries on the shelves, but we have none for ourselves,
There is mean things happening in this land.

There is mean things happening in this land. *(Repeat.)*
Oh, we'll have even less to eat when the drums commence to beat,
There is mean things happening in this land.

There is mean things happening in this land. *(Repeat.)*
But when the working men refuse to put on their old war shoes,
There'll be *good things* happening in this land.

There'll be *good things* happening in this land. *(Repeat.)*
When the workers take a stand and unite in a solid band,
There'll be *good things* happening in this land.

THREE GRAINS OF CORN

In a crisis of overproduction, hunger should have been unknown, but many first-generation Americans remembered hard times endured before. Iowa farmers might sing, "This is the land for corn and wheat, a land that never knew retreat," but memories of famine in Ireland produced this song.

Give me three grains of corn, Mother,
Only three grains of corn.
'Twill keep what little life I have
Till the coming of the morn.

For I'm dying of hunger and cold, Mother,
Dying of hunger and cold,
And the agony of such a death
My lips have never told.

Oh, what has old Ireland done, Mother,
Oh, what has old Ireland done,
That the world looks on and sees them starve,
Perishing one by one?

There is many a brave heart, Mother,
That is dying of hunger and cold,
While only across the channel, Mother,
Thousands are rolling their gold.

Oh, how can I look to you, Mother,
Oh, how can I look to you
For bread to feed your starving child
When you are starving too?

I dreamed of bread in my sleep, Mother,
The sight was heaven to see.
I awoke with an eager and famishing lip
And you had no bread for me.

BOLL WEEVIL SONG

That a highly destructive insect could be an economic savior is hard to believe, but a menace to cotton no one could buy proved a blessing. A statue in Alabama honors the bug who bored his way into basic economics.

Oh, de boll weevil am a little black bug,
Come from Mexico, dey say,
Come all de way to Texas, jus' a-lookin' foh a place to stay,
Jus' a-lookin' foh a home, jus' a-lookin' foh a home.

De first I seen de boll weevil,
He was a-settin' on de square.
De next time I seen de boll weevil, he had all of his family dere.
Jus' a-lookin' foh a home, jus' a-lookin' foh a home.

De farmer say to de weevil:
"What make yo' head so red?"
De weevil say to de farmer, "It's a wondah I ain't dead,
A-lookin' foh a home, jus' a-lookin' foh a home."

De farmer take de boll weevil,
An' he put him in de hot san'.
De weevil say: "Dis is mighty hot, but I'll stan' it like a man,
Dis'll be my home, dis'll be my home."

De farmer take de boll weevil,
An' he put him in a lump of ice;
De boll weevil say to de farmer: "Dis is mighty cool and nice,
Dis'll be my home, dis'll be my home."

De farmer take de boll weevil,
An' he put him in de fire.
De boll weevil say to de farmer: "Here I are, here I are,
Dis'll be my home, dis'll be my home."

De boll weevil say to de farmer:
"You better leave me alone;
I done eat all yo' cotton, now I'm goin' to start on yo' corn,
I'll have a home, I'll have a home."

De farmer say to de merchant:
"We's in an awful fix;
De boll weevil et all de cotton up an' lef' us only sticks,
We's got no home, we's got no home."

De farmer say to de merchant:
"We ain't made but only one bale,
And befoh we'll give yo' dat one we'll fight and go to jail,
We'll have a home, we'll have a home."

A MAN'S A MAN FOR A' THAT

Robert Burns wrote a song in defense of the victims of poverty, and in the hard times Earl Robinson set it to music. Except for the Scottish dialect, the lyric is one for today's changing world.

Is there for honest poverty, that hangs his head, and a' that?
The coward slave, we pass him by, we dare be poor for a' that.
For a' that, and a' that,
Our toil's obscure, and a' that,
The rank is but the guinea's stamp, the man's the gowd, for a' that.

What though on homely fare we dine, wear hodden gray, and a' that,
Give fools their silk and knaves their wine, a man's a man for a' that.
For a' that, and a' that,
Their tinsel show, and a' that,
The honest man though nae sae poor is king o' men for a' that.

Ye see yon birkie called a lord, who struts and stares and a' that,
Though hundreds worship at his word, he's but a fool for a' that.
For a' that and a' that,
His ribband star and a' that,
The man of independent mind, he looks and laughs at a' that.

A prince can make a belted knight, a marquis, duke and a' that,
But an honest man's above his might, good faith he keeps for a' that.
For a' that and a' that,
Their dignities and a' that,
The pith o' sense and pride o' worth are higher rank than a' that.

Then let us pray that come it may, as come it will for a' that,
That sense and worth o'er a' the earth shall win the fight for a' that.
For a' that and a' that,
It's comin' yet for a' that,
That man to man the world o'er, shall brothers be for a' that.

THE FARMER IS THE MAN

That tomatoes sold in the city for fifteen cents each can rot in a farmer's basket at a dollar a bushel is a familiar fact of life, but in good times or bad it causes comment. This song goes back to the Populist days and farm problems of the eighties.

When the farmer comes to town with his wagon broken down,
Oh, the farmer is the man who feeds them all.
If you'll only look and see, I think you will agree
That the farmer is the man who feeds them all.

Refrain:
The farmer is the man, the farmer is the man
Lives on credit till the fall.
Then they take him by the hand,
And they lead him from the land,
And the middleman's the one who gets it all.

When the farmer hangs around, while the butcher cuts a pound,
Oh, the farmer is the man who feeds them all.
While the preacher and the cook go a-strolling by the brook,
The farmer is the man who feeds them all.

Refrain:
The farmer is the man, the farmer is the man
Lives on credit till the fall.
With the int'rest rate so high,
It's a wonder he don't die,
For the mortgage man's the one who gets it all.

GOIN' DOWN THE ROAD

One remedy Americans have always found: move on. The shift of population from city to country has begun, but suburbia has not yet countered urbanization, and the roads now carry two-way traffic, with problems at both ends. Woody Guthrie wrote this one. Copyright 1960, 1963 by Hollis Music, Inc. All rights reserved. Used by permission.

I'm goin' down the road feelin' bad,
I'm goin' down the road feelin' bad.
I'm goin' down the road feelin' bad, Lord,
    Lord,
And I ain't gonna be treated this a-way.

I can't live on cornbread and beans . . .
Forty cents an hour won't pay my rent . . .

Two dollar shoes hurt my feet . . .
Five dollar shoes suits me fine . . .
I'm goin' where the chilly winds don't
    blow . . .
I'm goin' where the water tastes like wine . . .
That prison water tastes like turpentine . . .
I'm goin' where the climate suits my
    clothes . . .
Goin' down the road feelin' bad.

HARD TRAVELIN'

*Another Guthrie song, with a romantic twist at the end, was written for the road
but has been parodied for peace. Copyright 1959, 1963 by Ludlow Music, Inc.,
New York. All rights reserved. Used by permission.*

I been a-havin' some hard travelin',
I thought you knowed.
I been a-havin' some hard travelin',
Way down the road.
I been a-havin' some hard travelin',
Hard ramblin', hard gamblin',
I been a-havin' some hard travelin', Lord.

I been a-workin' in a hard rock tunnel,
I thought you knowed;
I been a-leanin' on a pressure drill,
Way down the road.
Hammer flyin', air hose suckin',
Six feet of mud, I sure been a-muckin',
I been a-havin' some hard travelin', Lord.

I been a-workin' that Pittsburgh steel,
I thought you knowed;
I been a-workin' that red-hot slag,
Way down the road.

I been a-blastin', I been a-firin',
I been a-duckin' red-hot iron,
I been a-havin' some hard travelin', Lord.

I been hittin' some hard harvestin',
I thought you knowed;
I been hittin' some rough handlin',
Way down the road;
Cut that wheat and stack that hay,
Tryin' to make about a dollar a day,
I been a-havin' some hard travelin', Lord.

I been a-hittin' that Lincoln Highway,
I thought you knowed;
I been a-hittin' that sixty-six,
Way down the road;
Heavy load and a worried mind,
Lookin' for a woman that's hard to find,
I been a-havin' some hard travelin', Lord.

THE TRAMP

*A similar theme is in this song written by Joe Hill and sung to the appropriate
Civil War tune "Tramp! Tramp! Tramp!"*

If you all will shut your trap,
I will tell you 'bout a chap
That was broke and up against it, too, for fair.
He was not the kind to shirk,
He was looking hard for work,
But he heard the same old story everywhere:

Chorus:
"Tramp, tramp, tramp, keep on a-tramping.
Nothing doing here for you.
If I catch you round again,
You will wear the ball and chain,
Keep on tramping, that's the best thing you can do."

He walked up and down the street,
Till the shoes fell off his feet;
In a house he spied a lady cooking stew.
And he said, "How do you do?
May I chop some wood for you?"
What the lady told him made him feel so blue:—*Cho.*

Finally came the happy day
When his life did pass away;
He was sure he'd go to heaven when he died.
When he reached the pearly gate
Santa Peter, mean old skate,
Slammed the gate right in his face, and loudly cried:—*Cho.*

HALLELUJAH, I'M A BUM!

In the depression days arrests for vagrancy, especially in the Far West, became a frequent device to halt unwanted immigration. Songs such as this one deplored the lack of hospitality.

Oh, why don't you work like other men do?
Oh, how can I work when there's no work to do?

Chorus:
Hallelujah, I'm a bum! Hallelujah, bum again!
Hallelujah, give us a handout, to revive us again.

Oh, I love my boss, and my boss loves me,
And that is the reason that I'm so hungry.
—*Cho.*

Oh, springtime has come, and I'm just out of jail,
Without any money, and without any bail.
—*Cho.*

I went to a house, and I knocked on the door,
A lady came out, says, "You been here before."
　　　　　　　　　　　　　　　—*Cho.*

I went to a house, and I asked for some bread;
A lady came out, says, "The baker is dead."
　　　　　　　　　　　　　　　—*Cho.*

When springtime does come, oh, won't we
　　have fun,
We'll throw up our jobs and we'll go on the
　bum.—*Cho.*

If I was to work, and save all I earn,
I could buy me a bar and have money to burn.
　　　　　　　　　　　　　　　—*Cho.*

THE ST. LOUIS BLUES

W. C. Handy wrote this first and most famous of the "Blues" in 1914—a year in a depression cycle, but not the worst. For southern Negroes, however, depression seemed a permanent part of life, and a popular theory is that the blues, musically, were protest songs. Copyright 1914 by W. C. Handy; used by permission of the Handy Brothers Music Company. All rights reserved.

I hate to see de evenin' sun go down
Hate to see de evenin' sun go down
'Cause ma baby, he done lef' dis town.
Feelin' tomorrow lak ah feel today
Feelin' tomorrow lak ah feel today
I'll pack ma trunk an' mak ma git away.

Chorus:
Got de St. Louis blues, jes blue as ah can be.
Dat man got a heart lak a rock cast in de sea.
Or else he wouldn' gone so far from me.

I loves dat man lak a schoolboy loves his pie,
Lak a Kentucky col'nel loves his mint an' rye.
I'll love ma baby till de day ah die.
　　　　　　　　　Doggone it! (spoken)

BROTHER, CAN YOU SPARE A DIME?

Those lucky enough to miss the depression can learn about it from this popular song, with music by Jay Gorney for the E. Y. Harburg lyric. Copyright 1932 by Harms, Inc. All rights reserved. Used by permission.

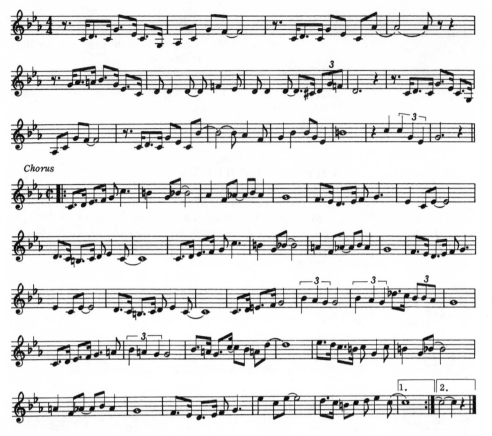

They used to tell me I was building a dream,
And so I followed the mob.
When there was earth to plough or guns
    to bear,
I was always there, right on the job.
They used to tell me I was building a dream
With peace and glory ahead.
Why should I be standing in line, just waiting
    for bread?

Chorus:
Once I built a railroad, now it's done—
Brother, can you spare a dime?
Once I built a tower to the sun—
Brick and rivet and lime.
Once I built a tower, now it's done—
Brother, can you spare a dime?

Once in khaki suits, gee, we looked swell
Full of that Yankee Doodle de dum.
Half a million boots went sloggin' through he
I was the kid with the drum.

Say, don't you remember, they called me Al—
It was Al all the time.
Say, don't you remember, I'm your pal—
Brother, can you spare a dime?

THE TVA SONG

Most successful of the efforts to lift the country out of the doldrums of the thirties was the Tennessee Valley Authority, which became an enduring asset to the country. This song followed the folk song tradition—no known author or composer, though it was widely quoted.

My name is William Edwards, I live down Cove Creek way.
I'm workin' on the project they call the TVA.
The government begun it when I was but a child,
But now they are in earnest and Tennessee's gone wild.

I see them boys a-comin', their tool kits on their arm;
They come from Clinch and Holston and many a valley farm.
All up and down the Valley they heard the glad alarm;
The government means business—it's workin' like a charm.

Oh, see the boys a-comin'—their government they trust.
Just hear their hammers singin'—they'll build that dam or bust.
I'm writing Sal a letter, these words I'll surely say:
"The government has saved us, just name our wedding day."

We'll build a little cabin, on Cove Creek near her home.
We'll settle down forever and never care to roam.
For things are surely movin' down there in Tennessee:
Good times for all the valley, for Sally and for me.

HARD TIMES COME AGAIN NO MORE

*Stephen Foster's song expresses the pious hope of his day and the very real hope
of those today who feel that the depression cycle can be broken, not merely once,
but once for all.*

Let us pause in life's pleasures, and count its many tears,
While we all sup sorrow with the poor.
There's a song that will linger forever in our ears,
"Oh! Hard times come again no more."

While we seek mirth and beauty, and music light and gay,
There are frail forms fainting at the door.
Though their voices are silent, their pleading looks will say,
"Oh! Hard times come again no more."

'Tis a sigh that is wafted across the troubled wave,
'Tis a wail that is heard upon the shore.
'Tis a dirge that is murmured around the lowly grave,
"Oh! Hard times come again no more."

VI

SONGS OF ESCAPE

Progress, as seen from the rear by those who stay behind, often looks like escape. It can be argued that the explorers and adventurers who seek new worlds are mainly motivated by some dissatisfaction with the old; this hardly matters if their search is successful or if, as often happens, they come to enjoy travel. Whether the traveler moves on to leave behind injustice or boredom, prejudice or failure, or to learn new ways and make new friends, the moving itself becomes important and has had encouragement from singers ever since the troubadours.

As the Western world was settled and claimed by migrants who moved on either to escape persecution or to better their fortunes,

it is only natural that the United States as a Western power should be subject to the charge of diverse motives and contradictory conduct. The dual heritage is here, as well as the fact that some movers and shakers attain results other than those intended.

As diverse as the motives for escape are the paths taken. There may be literal movement—on the road or across the sea. There may be the threat of pursuit, the rewards of travel or the mockery of hope, dreams shattered or dreams come true. After parting may come nostalgia for the familiar, concern for the old folks at home, or the temptation to forsake planned routes for companionship on old familiar roads. Songs have told it all, and more.

DANNY BOY

One of the oldest of all the world's recorded tunes, the "Londonderry Air" wears well. Of various lyrics, the one that means most today tells, in terms of the young Irish emigrant, the perennial story of parting to live in a new land. Irish Catholics emigrated to escape the Established Church, and today in Londonderry they still protest. Both Catholics and Protestants fled the potato famine. But Danny, whatever his motive, was leaving love behind, and those who go far from home know how that is. Lyric by Fred E. Weatherly. Copyright 1913, 1944 by Boosey & Company. All rights reserved. Used by permission.

Oh, Danny boy, the pipes, the pipes are calling,
From glen to glen, and down the mountainside.
The summer's gone, and all the roses falling,
It's you, it's you must go, and I must bide.

But come ye back, when summer's in the meadow,
Or when the valley's hushed and white with snow.
It's I'll be here, in sunshine or in shadow,
Oh, Danny boy, oh, Danny boy, I love you so!

But when ye come, and all the flow'rs are dying,
And I am dead, as all the flow'rs must die,
Ye'll come and find the place where I am lying,
And kneel and say an Ave where I lie.

And I shall hear, though soft you tread above me,
And in the dark my soul will wake and see.
For you'll bend down and tell me that you love me,
And we shall sleep in peace for all eternity.

WANDERIN'

There is in this country the migrant worker who as the seasons change goes, from choice or from necessity, from job to job across a big country. In this song he is on his own, but now the migrant workers are legion, and move in masses to wherever jobs are available.

My daddy is an engineer,
My brother drives a hack,
My sister takes in washin'
An' the baby balls the jack,
An' it looks like
I'm never gonna cease my wanderin'.

I been a wanderin'
Early and late,
New York City
To the Golden Gate,
An' it looks like
I'm never gonna cease my wanderin'.

Been a-workin' in the army,
Workin' on a farm,
All I got to show for it
Is the muscle in my arm,
An' it looks like
I'm never gonna cease my wanderin'.

STEAL AWAY

The original travelers from necessity, in this country, were those slaves who took the underground railway route before the Civil War. Some spirituals gave directions for going North.

My Lord calls me, he calls me by the thunder,
The trumpet sounds within-a my soul, I ain't got long to stay here

Chorus:
Steal away, steal away, steal away to Jesus!
Steal away, steal away home, I ain't got long to stay here.

Green trees are bending, poor sinner stands a-trembling.—*Cho.*

My Lord calls me, he calls me by the lightning.—*Cho.*

FOLLOW THE DRINKIN' GOURD

If anyone doubts the practical directions given by the slave songs, here is the evidence. The Gourd was, of course, the Dipper with its directions to the North Star. The same constellation aided the moonlight rebels of Ireland, who called it the Plough and the Stars, and put it on their flag.

When the sun comes back and the first quail calls,
Follow the drinkin' gourd,
For then the old man is a-waitin' for to carry you to freedom,
If you follow the drinkin' gourd.

Chorus:
Follow, follow, follow—follow the drinkin' gourd!
Follow the drinkin' gourd,
For the old man is a-waitin' for to carry you to freedom,
If you follow the drinkin' gourd.

The river bank will make a very good road,
The dead trees show you the way,
Left foot, peg foot, traveling on—
Follow the drinkin' gourd.—*Cho.*

The river ends between two hills,
Follow the drinkin' gourd,
There's another river on the other side,
Follow the drinkin' gourd.—*Cho.*

Where the great big river meets the little river,
Follow the drinkin' gourd,
The old man is a-waitin' for to carry you to freedom,
If you follow the drinkin' gourd.—*Cho.*

SWING LOW, SWEET CHARIOT

The religious meaning was home to heaven, but perhaps this old favorite also directed one to a constellation—was the "chariot" Charles's Wain?

I looked over Jordan and what did I see,
Comin' for to carry me home!
A band of angels comin' after me,
Comin' for to carry me home!

Chorus:
Swing low, sweet chariot,
Comin' for to carry me home!

Swing low, sweet chariot,
Comin' for to carry me home!

If you get there before I do,
Jes' tell my frien's that I'm comin' too.—*Cho.*

I'm sometimes up an' sometimes down.
But still my soul feels heavenly boun'.—*Cho.*

PHARAOH'S ARMY GOT DROWNDED

One problem of escape is possible pursuit; this spiritual, perhaps to hearten others, records one of the world's most fortunate escapes—described in the Book of Exodus.

If I could I surely would
Stan' on de rock where Moses stood.
Pharaoh's army got drownded,

Chorus:
O Mary, don' you weep, don' you mo'n.
O Mary, don' you weep, don' you mo'n.

O Mary, don' you weep, don' you mo'n.
Pharaoh's army got drownded.
O Mary, don' you weep, don' you mo'n.

Some o' these nights about twelve o'clock
Dis ol' worl' gwine to reel an' rock.
Pharaoh's army got drownded.—*Cho.*

GIVE MY REGARDS TO BROADWAY

As written and sung by George M. Cohan, this song perfectly expresses the very real nostalgia for their home town felt by New Yorkers in exile.

Give my regards to Broadway,
Remember me to Herald Square.
Tell all the gang at Forty-second Street
That I will soon be there.

Whisper of how I'm yearning
To mingle with the old-time throng.
Give my regards to old Broadway
And say I'll be there ere long.

HOME ON THE RANGE

White Americans free to leave usually went west after hearing promises such as this one in praise of the new country. Brewster Higley and Dan Kelly wrote it when animals seeking their own escape still bounded over the plains.

Oh, give me a home where the buffalo roam,
And the deer and the antelope play.
Where seldom is heard a discouraging word,
And the skies are not cloudy all day.

Home, home on the range
Where the deer and the antelope play,
Where seldom is heard a discouraging word
And the skies are not cloudy all day.

SWEET BETSY FROM PIKE

A western trek from Missouri's celebrated Pike County to the new land of opportunity out West was made by Betsy, Ike, and the livestock celebrated in this famous pioneer song. The many verses have no authors now known.

Oh, don't you remember sweet Betsy from Pike,
Who crossed the big mountains with her lover Ike,
With two yoke of cattle, a large yellow dog,
A tall shanghai rooster and a one-spotted hog.

Chorus:
Singin' Tooral lal looral lal looral lal la,
Tooral lal looral lal looral lal la.

The shanghai ran off and their cattle all died,
That morning the last piece of bacon was fried;
Poor Ike was discouraged and Betsy got mad,
The dog drooped his tail and looked wondrously sad.—*Cho.*

They soon reached the desert, where Betsy gave out,
And down in the sand she lay rolling about;
While Ike, half distracted, looked on with surprise,
Saying, "Betsy, get up, you'll get sand in your eyes."—*Cho.*

Sweet Betsy got up in a great deal of pain,
Declared she'd go back to Pike County again;
But Ike gave a sigh, and they fondly embraced,
And they traveled along with his arm 'round her waist.—*Cho.*

This Pike County couple got married of course,
But Ike became jealous, obtained a divorce;
Sweet Betsy, well satisfied, said with a great shout,
"Good-by, you big lummox, I'm glad you've backed out!"—*Cho.*

GYPSY DAVY

The gypsy strain moves through many folk songs; this English song begins a story that is retold with variations in the one that follows.

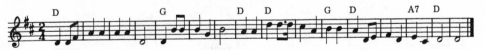

I was a high-born gentleman,
She was a high-born lady.
We lived in a palace great and tall,
Till she met with Gypsy Davy.

Last night she slept in a goose-feather bed,
With her arms around her baby.
Tonight she lies in the cold, cold ground
In the arms of her Gypsy Davy.

THE WRAGGLE-TAGGLE GYPSIES

Some people just like to travel, and in this version the runaway lady apparently has chosen the gypsy life rather than another man.

There were three gypsies came to my door,
And downstairs ran this lady-o.
One sang high and the other sang low,
And the third sang bonny, bonny Biscay-O!

Then she pulled off her silk-finished gown,
And put on hose of leather-O!
The ragged, ragged rags about our door,
And she's gone with the wraggle-taggle
    Gypsies O!

It was late last night when my Lord came home,
Inquiring for his a-lady, O!
The servants said on ev'ry hand:
She's gone with the wraggle-taggle Gypsies O!

O saddle to me my milk-white steed,
And go fetch me my pony, O!
That I may ride and seek my bride,
Who is gone with the wraggle-taggle
    Gypsies O!

O he rode high, and he rode low,
He rode through wood and copses too,

Until he came to a wide open field,
And there he espied his a-lady, O!

What makes you leave your house and land?
What makes you leave your money O!
What makes you leave your new-wedded Lord?
I'm off with the wraggle-taggle Gypsies O!

What care I for my house and land?
What care I for my money, O!
What care I for my new-wedded Lord?
I'm off with the wraggle-taggle Gypsies O!

Last night you slept on a goose-feather bed,
With the sheet turned down so bravely-O!
Tonight you'll sleep in a cold, open field,
Along with the wraggle-taggle Gypsies O!

What care I for a goose-feather bed,
With the sheet turned down so bravely-O!
For tonight I shall sleep in a cold, open field,
Along with the wraggle-taggle Gypsies O!

THE GYPSY TRAIL

*Rudyard Kipling's romantic ballad, with music by Tod B. Galloway, was a great
success in its day and can still hold its own among the travel songs.*

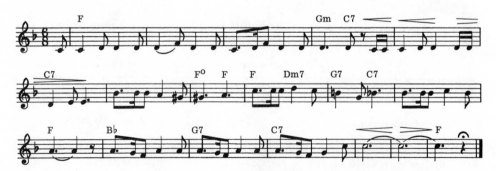

The white moth to the closing vine.
The bee to the opening clover,
And the gypsy blood to the gypsy blood,
Ever the wide world over.

Chorus:
Ever the wide world over, lass—
Ever the trail held true.

Over the world and under the world,
And back at the last to you.

Out of the dust of the gorgio camp,
Out of the grime and the gray,
Morning waits at the end of the world—
Gypsy, come away.

Back to the road again, again,
Out on a clean sea track
Follow the cross of the gypsy trail
Over the world and back.

Follow the Romany patteran
West to the sinking sun
Till the junk sails lift to the homeless drift
And the East and the West are one.

Follow the Romany patteran
East where the silence broods,

By a purple wave on an opal beach,
In the hush of the Mahim woods.

The wild hawk to the windswept sky,
The deer to the wholesome wold,
And the heart of a man to the heart of a maid
As it was in the days of old.

The heart of a man to the heart of a maid—
Light of my tents, be fleet.
Morning waits at the end of the world,
And the world is at our feet.

THE BIG ROCK CANDY MOUNTAIN

A goal for the wanderer could be a never-never land such as this one, with no known author and volunteer verses added in true folk-song style. It was a request number on Pete Seeger's tour of the Soviet Union.

One evening as the sun went down,
And the jungle fires were burning,
Down the track comes a hobo hiking,
And he said "Boys, I'm not turning.
I'm headed for a land that's far away
Beside the crystal fountain,
I'll see you all this coming fall
In the Big Rock Candy Mountain."

Chorus:
In the Big Rock Candy Mountain
There's a land that's fair and bright,
Where the handouts grow on bushes
And you sleep out every night.
Where the boxcars all are empty
And the sun shines every day,
Oh, the birds and the bees
And the cigarette trees,
The rock 'n' rye springs
Where the whang doodle sings
In the Big Rock Candy Mountain!

THE MAN WHO BROKE THE BANK AT MONTE CARLO

Here the dream is no more practical, although the British traveler made his expenses abroad and a bit over. Words and music by the English songwriter Fred Gilbert.

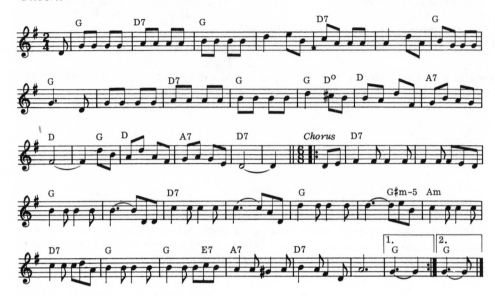

I've just got here, through Paris, from the sunny southern shore;
I to Monte Carlo went, just to raise my winter's rent;
Dame Fortune smiled upon me as she'd never done before,
And I've now such lots of money I'm a gent.
Yes, I've now such lots of money I'm a gent.

Chorus:
As I walk along the Bois Boolong with an independent air,
You can hear the girls declare, "He must be a millionaire."
You can hear them sigh, and wish to die,
You can see them wink the other eye
At the man that broke the bank at Monte Carlo.

HOME, SWEET HOME

The trouble with travel, as many escapists discover, is the gravity pull back home. These familiar words were written by John Howard Paine; the music is by Sir Henry Bishop, who back in 1814 conducted the London Philharmonic.

'Mid pleasures and palaces though we may roam,
Be it ever so humble, there's no place like home.
A charm from the skies seems to hallow us there,
Which, seek through the world, is not met with elsewhere.

Refrain:

Home, home, sweet, sweet home,
There's no place like home,
Oh, there's no place like home.

I gaze on the moon as I tread the drear wild,
And feel that my mother now thinks of her child.
As she looks on that moon from her own cottage door,
Through the woodbine whose fragrance shall cheer me no more.—*Ref.*

An exile from home, splendor dazzles in vain;
Oh, give me my lowly thatched cottage again.
The birds singing gaily that came at my call,
Give me them, and that peace of mind dearer than all.—*Ref.*

OLD FOLKS AT HOME

Here in Stephen Foster's song is the ultimate reason for the prodigal's return. Almost a folk song by popular identification, this, like other Stephen Foster music, obviously owes much to Negro influence.

Way down upon the Swanee River,
Far, far, away,
There's where my heart is turning ever,
There's where the old folks stay.
All up and down the whole creation,
Sadly I roam,
Still longing for the old plantation,
And for the old folks at home.

Chorus:
All the world am dark and dreary,
Ev'rywhere I roam.·
Oh, darkies, how my heart grows weary,
Far from the old folks at home.

One little hut among the bushes,
One that I love
Still sadly to my mem'ry rushes,
No matter where I rove.
When shall I see the bees a-humming
All round the comb?
When shall I hear the banjo thrumming
Down in my good old home?—*Cho.*

GOODBYE, BROTHER

This song of parting is almost certainly an earthly one, another "Danny Boy" for those about to leave—unless it is read as a brave farewell to a slave sold "down the river."

Goodbye, brother, goodbye, brother,
If I don't see you more;
Now God bless you, now God bless you,
If I don't see you more.

We part in de body, but we meet in de spirit,
If I don't see you more;

We'll meet in de heaben, in de blessed kingdom,
If I don't see you more.

So goodbye brother, goodbye sister,
If I don't see you more;
Now God bless you, now God bless you,
If I don't see you more.

LOCH LOMOND

As for company on the road, this old Scottish folk song, of unclaimed origin, puts the travel problem: If one takes the high road and one the low, it has to be goodbye.

By yon bonnie banks and by yon bonnie braes,
Where the sun shines bright on Loch Lomon',
Where me and my true love were ever wont to gae,
On the bonnie, bonnie banks of Loch Lomon'.

Faster:
Oh! ye'll tak' the high road and I'll tak' the low road,
And I'll be in Scotland afore ye.
But me and my true love will never meet again
On the bonnie, bonnie banks of Loch Lomon'.

'Twas there that we parted in yon shady glen,
On the steep, steep side o' Ben Lomon'.
Where in purple hue the Hieland hills we view,
And the moon coming out in the gloamin'.

The wee birdies sing and the wild flowers spring,
And in sunshine the waters are sleepin',
But the broken heart it kens nae second spring again,
Though the waefu' may cease frae their greetin'.

VII

RELIGIOUS SONGS

The "song of Deborah" (Judges 5) in the Old Testament is presumably the oldest recorded song in Judeo-Christian culture. Musically the oldest survivors are the Gregorian chants, many of which supplied themes for today's hymnals. Music cannot be confined by creeds; Palestrina is heard in Protestant hymns sung in churches where his contribution to musical history is unknown. Of American hymns, greatest credit belongs to the Negro spirituals, whose significant meaning continues even as circumstances change. And as the scriptural heritage is shared, even the words of the best-loved hymns are echoed in Jewish and Christian hymns, in both Catholic and Protestant churches, and in the spirituals.

Whether by words or by music, and preferably by both together, religious songs have long moved the world—sometimes as reminders of an ancient faith, often as inspirations to change. Hymns heard in childhood influence individual responses in later life, while mass singing by religious groups has its own emotional appeal. In today's world we have few new songs about religion, if we do not count those considered to be against religion because they criticize established order. But such criticism is not new, and resultant change in religious establishments has often confirmed as doctrine what once was considered heresy. Today we can see increasing religious involvement in world problems, and also in exchange of ideas between groups formerly opposed or indifferent to each other's teaching. This already encourages a discard of narrowly doctrinal songs in favor of those making music the language of faith and hope. As an example of ecumenical harmony, at Christmas, 1967, the bells of St. Patrick's in New York played the old tune which, though it began as a Gregorian chant, is best known as "Luther's Hymn," Ein' Feste Burg.

ROCK OF AGES (Mo'oz Tsur)

This name was given to hymns in both Jewish and Christian worship; appropriately, the older one begins this section. Its composer unknown, the song is familiar in Jewish households.

Rock of Ages, let our song
Praise Thy saving power.
Thou amidst the raging foes
Wast our shelt'ring tower.
Furious they assailed up,
But Thine arm availed us,
And Thy Word
Broke their sword
When our own strength failed us.

Children of the Martyr-race,
Whether free or fettered,
Wake the echoes of the songs
Where ye may be scattered.
Yours the message cheering
That the time is nearing
Which will see
All men free,
Tyrants disappearing.

Mo'oz tsur y'shuosee, l'cho noeh l'shabeyach,
Tikon beys t'filosee v'shom todoh n'zabeyach;
L'eys tocheen matbeyach mitsor ha'm'na-beyach,
Oz egmor b'sheer mizmor, chanukas hamiz-beyach.

Y'voneem nikb'tsu olai azai beemey chashma-neem;
Ufortsu chomos migdolai v'tim'u chol hash-moneem;
Uminosar kankaneem naasoh neys l'shosha-neem.
B'ney veenoh y'mey sh'monoh kov'u sheer ur'noneem.

ADESTE FIDELES
(O Come, All Ye Faithful)

"O Come, All Ye Faithful" is often sung in Latin by Catholics and in English by Protestants; it is indeed a song of faith in and loyalty to the Christian tenets as accepted by all believers in the creed.

O come, all ye faithful, joyful and triumphant,
O come ye, O come ye to Bethlehem.
Come and behold him, monarch of the angels.
O come, let us adore him;
O come, let us adore him;
O come, let us adore him, Christ the Lord.
Sing allelulia, all ye choirs of angels;
O sing, all ye blissful ones of heaven above.
Glory to God, in the highest, glory!
O come, etc.

Adeste fideles, laeti triumphantes,
Venite, venite in Bethlehem!
Natum venite, regem angelorum!
Venite, adoremus;
Venite, adoremus;
Venite, adoremus, Dominum.

EIN' FESTE BURG

Luther's hymn has undergone many changes. The first version given here, written in 1529, is still sung; it was known in Victorian times as "Albert's favorite hymn." The second is a modern version by Frederick Root. The third, a humanist variant by Kenneth L. Patton, was sung in a Christmas peace demonstration in Times Square.

A mighty fortress is our God,
A bulwark never failing;
Our helper He amid the flood
Of mortal ills prevailing.
For still our ancient foe
Doth seek to work us woe—
His craft and power are great,
And armed with cruel hate.
On earth is not his equal.

Did we in our own strength confide,
Our striving would be losing.
Were not the right man on our side,
The man of God's own choosing.

Dost ask who that may be?
Christ Jesus it is He,
Lord Sabaoth His name,
From age to age the same,
And he must win the battle.

And though this world with devils filled
Should threaten to undo us,
We will not fear, for God hath willed
His truth to triumph through us.
The Prince of Darkness grim,
We tremble not for him;
His rage we can endure,
For lo! his doom is sure.
One little word shall fell him.

That word above all earthly powers,
No thanks to them, abideth.
The spirit and the gifts are ours,
Through Him who with us sideth.
Let goods and kindred go,

This mortal life also,
The body they may kill,
God's truth abideth still.
His kingdom is forever.

LEAD, KINDLY LIGHT

Newman's hymn is found in both Protestant and Catholic hymnals because Cardinal Newman began his religious life in the Episcopal Church, and then became a convert to Rome. Music by John B. Dykes.

Lead, kindly Light, amid th' encircling gloom.
Lead Thou me on!
The night is dark, and I am far from home.
Lead Thou me on!
Keep Thou my feet; I do not ask to see
The distant scene—one step enough for me.

I was not ever thus, nor prayed that Thou
Shouldst lead me on;
I love to choose and see my path; but now
Lead Thou me on!

I loved the garish day, and spite of fears
Pride ruled my will—remember not past years.

So long Thy pow'r hath blest me, sure it still
Will lead me on
O'er moor and fen, o'er crag and torrent, till
The night is gone.
And with the morn those angel faces smile
Which I have loved long since, and lost
   awhile.

BATTLE HYMN OF THE HUSSITES
(Kdož Jste Boží Bojovníci)

The early fighting aspect of Protestant Christianity is well represented by this song, relied upon by the followers of Jan Huss to bring them victory in the religious wars of the Reformation.

Warriors of the Lord Almighty
And of His divine law,
For His help pray with submission,
In faith unto Him draw.
You shall receive from Him the crown of
   glory.

Foes for us can have no terror
Whatever their power.
In your heart retain the Lord God
Before whom they cower;
Never retreat nor falter in the battle.

Onward march in joy uplifted,
The foe we will shatter;
To the hilt let hands be welded,
'Fore God's name they scatter!
Kill them, destroy them! let not one escape us!

Kdož jste Boží bojovníci,
A zákona jeho,
Proste od Boha pomoci,
a doufejte v Něho
Že konečně s Ním vždycky zvítězíte.

ONWARD, CHRISTIAN SOLDIERS

Sullivan's stirring music is today more appreciated than the words, which to many hearers have too martial a sound. An early antiwar version, "Forward All Ye Faithful," is found among the peace songs in this book, as well as a satiric parody, "Christians at War."

Onward, Christian soldiers, marching as to war,
With the cross of Jesus going on before!
Christ, the royal master, leads against the foe;
Forward into battle, see His banners go.

Chorus:
Onward, Christian soldiers, marching as to war
With the cross of Jesus going on before!

Like a mighty army moves the church of God,
Brethren, we are treading where the saints have trod.
We are not divided, all one Body we,
One in hope and doctrine, one in charity.—*Cho.*

Crowns and thrones may perish, kingdoms rise and wane
But the Church of Jesus constant will remain;
Gates of hell can never 'gainst the Church prevail;
We have Christ's own promise, and that cannot fail.—*Cho.*

Onward, then, ye people! join our happy throng!
Blend with ours your voices in the triumph song!
Glory, laud, and honor, unto Christ the King,
This through countless ages men and angels sing.—*Cho.*

THAT OLD-TIME RELIGION

Often considered a "spiritual," this was also a song for revival meetings held by white Protestants in the South.

Gimme dat ol' time religion, gimme dat ol' time religion,
Gimme dat ol' time religion, it's good enough for me.

It was good for de Hebrew chillun, it was good, etc.
It was good for de Hebrew chillun, so it's good enough for me.

It was good for Paul and Aaron, it was good, etc.
It was good for Paul and Aaron, so it's good enough for me.

It'll be good when the worl's on fire, it'll be good, etc.
It'll be good when the worl's on fire, so it's good enough for me.

NETHERLANDS PRAYER OF THANKSGIVING

Heard today in homes where religious songs are seldom sung, this traditional song is a part of Thanksgiving festivities in many American households.

We gather together to ask the Lord's blessing.
He chastens and hastens His will to make known.
The wicked oppressing, cease them from distressing;
Sing praises to His name, He forgets not His own.

PRAISE GOD FROM WHOM ALL BLESSINGS FLOW
("Old Hundred"—The Doxology)

Otherwise known as "The Doxology," this, like the Latin Te Deum, *is also a psalm of thanksgiving. Words by Thomas Ken, music by Louis Bourgeois.*

Praise God, from Whom all blessings flow;
Praise Him, all creatures here below;
Praise Him above, ye heav'nly host;
Praise Father, Son, and Holy Ghost.

NOW THE DAY IS OVER

A favorite for evensong in the Church of England, this one has been called "Disraeli's favorite hymn." Sabine Baring-Gould wrote the words; the music is by Joseph Barnby.

Now the day is over,
Night is drawing nigh.
Shadows of the evening
Steal across the sky.
Now the darkness deepens,
Stars begin to peep.
Birds and beasts and flowers
Soon will be asleep.

Jesus, give the weary
Calm and sweet repose,
With Thy ten'drest blessing
May our eyelids close.
When the morning wakens,
Then may we arise
Pure and fresh and sinless
In Thy holy eyes.

THE LANDING OF THE PILGRIMS

In one sense a secular song, this New England favorite is also evidence of the religious motive in American settlement. The lyric is by Felicia Hemans, the music by A. Browne.

The breaking waves dashed high,
On a stern and rockbound coast,
And the woods against a stormy sky
Their giant branches tossed;
And the heavy night hung dark
The hills and waters o'er,
When a band of exiles moored their bark
On the wild New England shore.

Not as the conqueror comes
They, the true-hearted, came;
Not with the roll of stirring drums
And the trumpet that sings of fame;
Not as the flying come,
In silence and in fear;
They shook the depths of the desert gloom
With their hymns of lofty cheer.

THE ABOLITIONIST HYMN

That churches in the North took a stand in the Civil War affords a historic precedent for religious action in today's movements for equality of opportunity.

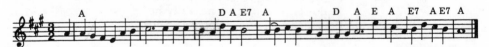

We ask not that the slave should lie,
As lies his master, at his ease,
Beneath a silken canopy
Or in the shade of blooming trees.
We ask not "eye for eye" that all
Who forge the chain and ply the whip

Should feel their torture, while the thrall
Should wield the scourge of mastership.
We mourn not that the man should toil:
'Tis Nature's need, 'tis God's decree.
But let the hand that tills the soil
Be, like the wind that fans it, free.

THESE THINGS SHALL BE

Transcendentalism, a religious faith in the future that seeks adjustment to the theory of evolution newly propounded, is well represented by this song with a lyric by John Addington Symonds.

These things shall be; a loftier race
Than e'er the world hath known shall rise,
With flame of freedom in their souls
And light of knowledge in their eyes.

Nation with nation, land with land,
Unarmed shall live as comrades free;
In every heart and brain shall throb
The pulse of one fraternity.

Man shall love man with heart as pure
And fervent as the young-eyed throng
Who chant their heavenly psalm before
God's face with undiscordant song.

New arts shall bloom of loftier mould,
And mightier music thrill the skies,
And every life shall be a song,
When all the earth is paradise.

JERUSALEM THE GOLDEN

Here we have almost a duplication of title between this Christian hymn about a heavenly hereafter, written in 1150 by St. Bernard of Clairvaux and set to music by Alexander Ewing, and today's deservedly popular song about modern Israel.

Jerusalem the golden! With milk and honey blest,
Beneath thy contemplation sink heart and voice oppress'd.
There is the throne of David, and there from toil released
The shout of them that triumph, the song of them that feast.

They stand, those halls of Zion, all jubilant with song,
And bright with many an angel, and all the martyr throng.
Oh, land that see'st no sorrow! Oh, state that fear'st no strife!
Oh, royal land of flowers! Oh, realm and home of life!

WHEN THE SAINTS GO MARCHING IN

A literal view of heaven expressed in this old song may have helped bring its share of unbelievers to the "mourners' bench" of repentance. Later, it would reach modern hearers on TV.

And when the Saints go marching in,
And when the Saints go marching in,
Lord, how I want to be in that number,
When the Saints go marching in.

And when the revelation comes,
And when the revelation comes,
Lord, how I want to be in that number,
When the revelation comes.

And when the new world is revealed, etc.

And when the sun refuse to shine, etc.

And when the moon has turned to blood, etc.

And when they gather round the throne, etc.

And when they crown him King of Kings, etc.

And on that hallelujah day, etc.

And when the Saints go marching in, etc.

LOOK DOWN THAT LONESOME ROAD

*A corollary spiritual warned against "freethinking" at a time when salvation was
identified with publicly professed acceptance of religious orthodoxy.*

Look down, look down, that lonesome road,
Before you trabble on.
Look up, look up, and greet your Maker,
'For Gabriel blows his horn.

Look down, look down, weary tredging on
   and on,
Tredging down that lonesome road.
Look up, look up, and greet your Maker,
'For Gabriel blows his horn.

WE WILL MARCH THROUGH THE VALLEY

*Today's marchers can still gain resolution from this spiritual, which dates from
the early struggles for human rights.*

We will march through the valley in peace,
We will march through the valley in peace.

If Jesus himself be our leader,
We will march through the valley in peace.

I DON'T FEEL NOWAYS TIRED

*Modern marchers can be cheered, it has been discovered, by musical declarations
such as this one from an earlier period.*

I don't feel weary and noways tired,
O glory hallelujah.
Jest let me in the kingdom
While the world is all on fire,
O glory hallelujah.

Gwine to walk with God forever while, etc.

And keep the ark a-moving while, etc.

MY LORD DELIBERED DANIEL

Here is real faith, and the line about John the Baptist brought down the house nightly when this spiritual was sung on Broadway in the play "Dark of the Moon."

My Lord delibered Daniel,
My Lord delibered Daniel,
My Lord delibered Daniel,
Why can't he deliber me?
I met a pilgrim on de way, an' I ask him whar
    he's gwine.
I'm bound for Canaan's happy land, and dis
    is de shoutin' band.

Some say dat John de Baptist
Was nothing but a Jew,
But de Bible doth inform us
Dat he was a preacher, too;
Yes, he was!
Cho.—My Lord delibered Daniel.

Oh, Daniel cast in de lions' den,
He pray both night an' day,
De angel came from Galilee,
An' lock de lions' jaw.
Dat's so.
Cho.—My Lord delibered Daniel.

He delibered Daniel from de lions' den,
Jonah from de belly ob de whale,
And de Hebrew children from de fiery
    furnace,
And why not ebery man?
Oh, yes!
Cho.—My Lord delibered Daniel.

I AM A LITTLE CHRISTIAN

Discovered by the WPA music project of the thirties, this innocently smug little song has no known authors. The project supervisor for Rowan County, Kentucky, was Lyda Messer Caudill.

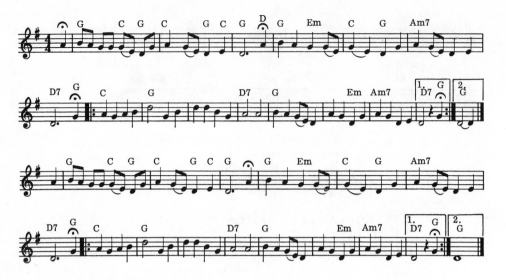

I am a little Christian.
The Lord has made me so.
All through these hills and valleys
What wonders he can do.
I love the things I hated.
I hate the things I love.
The Lord is now preparing me
To reign with him above.

I am a little soldier.
I've enlisted in the war
To fight my Master's battle
Till I can fight no more.

And when my war is ended
I'll lay my armor down
And fly away to heaven
And wear a starry crown.

I am a little watchman.
I stand on Zion's wall,
And when the foe is coming,
I give one loudly call.
I blow my little trumpet
To let the people know.
Come all you careless sinners,
Escape from every foe.

I GOT SHOES

Another spiritual contains the briefest and perhaps the best of religious criticism
—all the folks talkin' 'bout heab'n maybe ain't gwine dar.

I got a shoe, you got a shoe,
All God's chillun got shoes;
When I get to hebben, gwine a-put on my
    shoes,

Gwine-a tromp all over God's hebben.
Hebben, hebben;
Everybody talkin' about hebben, ain't a-gwine
    dar,

Hebben, hebben;
Gwine a-tromp all over God's hebben.

I got a robe, etc.
Gwine a-shout all over God's hebben.

I got a harp, etc.
Gwine a-play it all over God's hebben.

I got wings, etc.
Gwine a-fly all over God's hebben.

I got a song, etc.
Gwine a-sing all over God's hebben.

TALKING DEATH OF GOD

This song of today by Tom Paxton might be considered the reverse of a spiritual, until you look carefully at the last line. Copyright 1966 by Deep Fork Music, Inc. All rights reserved. Used by permission.

I went to church last week;
A hip young preacher I chanced to meet,
Rimless glasses, very long hair, a manner very
    debonair,
Reading Camus, taking trips,
Said, "Religion is where it's at, baby."

I told him I was sick at heart
With troubles tearing me apart,
With troubles growing worse each day
I felt the time had come to pray,
He said, "To whom?" "To God"
"Sorry. He's checked out."

I mean to tell you I was shook.
He said, "You'll have to read my book.
It puts the whole thing where it's at,
Friend, God is dead and that is that.
I was there. I waited around for three days
And when nothing happened I spread the
    word."

He said, "You're not the only one,
You know, who's looking glum.
My troubles, Friend, are really big
It looks like I've just blown my gig,

Me and Billy Graham, Norman Vincent
Peale, Lyndon B. Johnson."

One question I just had to try,
"Just how exactly did He die?"
He smiled and gently raised his hand.
"Some things we cannot understand.
Some mysteries are eternal. . . .
My eyes were blinded by holy fire,
And besides, I didn't want to hang around
To meet the one that did it."

Well, now he had me on the ropes,
I said goodbye to all my hopes,
But late that night I hit the floor
And thought that I would try once more.
A voice said, "Whom did you wish to
    speak to?"
"I'd like to speak to God."
"I'm sorry, that is not a working number.'

Then, just as I got off my knees
A streak of lightning hit a tree
The tree knocked down a high power wire
And set the whole damn town on fire,
Blew out the church's neon sign
Then it lit back up, sayin',
"I've got you covered."

THE VICAR OF BRAY

Here is a song to prove that skepticism and criticism do not constitute a new movement—both were long familiar in the English Establishment.

In good King Charles's golden days,
When loyalty no harm meant,
A zealous High-Churchman I was
And so I gained preferment;
To teach my flock I never missed—
Kings are by God appointed,
And damned are those who dare resist,
Or touch the Lord's anointed.

Chorus:
And this is law, I will maintain,
Until my dying day, Sir,
That whatsoever king shall reign,
I'll be the Vicar of Bray, Sir!

When royal James obtained the crown,
And Popery came in fashion,
The penal laws I hooted down,
And read the declaration:
The Church of Rome I found would fit
Full well my Constitution,
And I had been a Jesuit—
But for the Revolution.—*Cho.*

When William was our king declared
To heal the nation's grievance,
With this new wind about I steered,
And swore to him Allegiance:
Old principles I did revoke,
Set conscience at a distance,
Passive obedience was a joke,
A jest was non-resistance.—*Cho.*

When gracious Anne became our queen,
The Church of England's glory,
Another face of things was seen—
And I became a Tory:
Occasional Conformists base,
I scorned their moderation,
And thought the Church in danger was
From such prevarication.—*Cho.*

When George in pudding-time came o'er,
And moderate men looked big, Sir,
I turned the cat-in-pan once more—
And so became a Whig, Sir:
And this preferment I procured,
From our new faith's defender,
And almost every day abjured
The Pope and the Pretender.—*Cho.*

The illustrious House of Hanover,
And Protestant succession,
To these I lustily will swear—
While they can keep possession:
For in my faith and loyalty
I never once will falter,
And George my lawful King shall be—
Except the times should alter.—*Cho.*

PIE IN THE SKY

Early criticism of the older type of religious teaching, expressed by workers in this I.W.W. song, no doubt had some effect in turning today's churches toward movements for social and political change.

Long-haired preachers come out ev'ry night,
Try to tell you what's wrong and what's right;
But when asked how 'bout something to eat
They will answer with voices so sweet:

Refrain:
You will eat, bye and bye,
In that glorious land above the sky;
Work and pray, live on hay,
You'll get pie in the sky when you die.

If you fight hard for children and wife—
Try to get something good in this life—
You're a sinner and bad man, they tell,
When you die you will sure go to hell.—*Ref.*

Workingmen of all countries, unite,
Side by side we for freedom will fight:
When the world and its wealth we have
    gained,
To the grafters we'll sing this refrain:

RAGUPATI RA GAVA RAJAH RAM
(Rama, King of the Solar Race)

For world religionists, here is a favorite song of Mahatma Gandhi—asking "Who is Allah and who is Ram?" and so in effect urging agreement, rather than argument, in India and elsewhere, over different names given to God.

Ragupati ra gava rajah—Ram.
Pahtita phavana Sita Ram.
Sita Ram jay Sita Ram,
Pahtita phavana Sita Ram.
Ishwra Allah tere nam
Tubko sunmutti de bhagavan.

Free translation: Rama, King of the solar race;
Sita and Rama, saviours of the fallen.
Sita, Rama, Hail Sita, Rama.

IT'S A-ME, O LORD . . .
Standin' In The Need of Pray'r

In the end, when religion becomes a matter for personal decision, this spiritual well expresses a human need.

It's a-me, it's a-me, O Lord,
Standin' in the need of prayer, yes, Lord!
It's a-me, it's a-me, O Lord,
Standin' in the need of pray'r (of pray'r).

Not my brother (no), it's a-me, O Lord,

Not my sister, it's a-me, O Lord,
Standin' in the need of pray'r,

Not my father (no), it's a-me, O Lord,
Not my mother, it's a-me, O Lord,
Standin' in the need of pray'r.

VIII

POLITICAL SONGS

Roman street songs lampooned the Caesars, and Mother Goose rhymes reflected English politics—the frog who would a-wooing go was Queen Elizabeth's French suitor, and the rocking cradle held an insecure Baby Stuart. W. S. Gilbert carried the political double-talk into Victorian times; the Admiral in *Pinafore* was a landlubber appointee. Today's political satires are heard at Gridiron dinners and on campuses from New Hampshire to California, while the program of a White House concert to entertain British guests must tactfully omit "I Got Plenty o' Nothin'" and "The Road to Mandalay." But the songs that have, in some cases at least, made bids for direct influence on the public mind are of course the campaign songs.

In general the Democrats have had better luck in taking over popular music. If "The Sidewalks of New York" failed to elect Al Smith, "Happy Days Are Here Again" and "Hello, Lyndon" won out, and the three songs had a common denominator of popular cheer. "Oh! Susanna" for the GOP might seem to be in the same category, but the words "don't you cry" did not prove to be reassuring; the Republicans were wooing the South, but that year she wasn't to be won. "Hail, Hail, the Gang's All Here" sounds happy, with music by Sir Arthur Sullivan and the party lyric by Theodore F. Morse. However, it turned out that the music reminded many voters of the original Gilbert chorus from *The Pirates of Penzance,* which proposed to "vary piracee with a little burglaree," and those voters also remembered Teapot Dome.

At least two losing campaigns by minorit groups involved the animal kingdom. Cham Clark lost to Woodrow Wilson with no hel from the song that insisted "They Gotta Qui Kickin' My Dawg Around"—the dog under stood to be the Common People, victimize by Vested Interests. And Theodore Roosevelt third party had no luck with its clumsy parod of an old hymn that began "I want to be Bull Moose and with the Bull Moose stand.

With professional handling of publicity campaign songs may go the way of torchligh processions; but protest songs from the gras roots—the grass on campuses—now deal wit politics from many different angles. Variou "backlashes" make it difficult to gauge appeal as always when voters regroup. Newly enfran chised women delegates at national conven tions were not flattered when bands playe "Oh, You Beautiful Doll" and "La Donna Mobile." Today the efforts to gain Negr support may prove similarly clumsy; "Back lash Blues," a last poem by Langston Hughe not as yet set to music, suggests it:

"Mister Backlash, Mister Backlash,
Just who do you think I am?
You raise my taxes, freeze my wages,
Send my son to Vietnam. . . ."

As for the unpredictable women, two o them—"Sagittarius" in England and Malvin Reynolds in this country—are writing today Gilbertian verses on current politics. And th other new voters, the young? As the man wh organized the Beatles' concerts put it, "The could sway a presidential election if the wanted to."

HAIL TO THE CHIEF

To some Americans it may seem surprising that their Presidents should be greeted by a song written by Sir Walter Scott. The music is by James Sanderson.

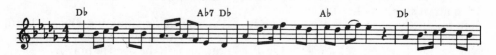

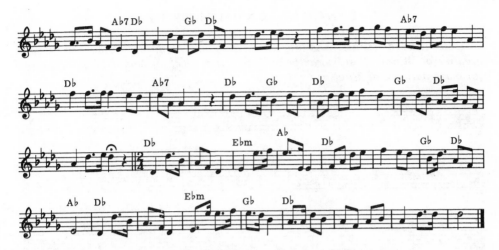

Hail to the Chief, who in triumph advances,
Honored and blessed be the evergreen pine.
Long may the tree in his banner that glances
Flourish, the shelter and grace of our line.
(Repeat.)

Heaven send it happy dew,
Earth lend it sap anew,
Gaily to burgeon and broadly to grow;
While every highland glen
Sends our shout back again,
"Roderigh Vich Alpine dhu, ho! i-e-roe!"

JEFFERSON AND LIBERTY

In the last verse we have, for the election of 1800, a promise yet to be realized, although New Deal projects during the depression, and government plans under President Kennedy, did acknowledge the arts.

The gloomy night before us flies,
The reign of terror now is o'er;
Its gangs, inquisitors and spies,
Its herds of harpies are no more.

Chorus:
Rejoice, Columbia's sons, rejoice;
To tyrants never bend the knee
But join with heart and soul and voice
For Jefferson and liberty.

No lordling here, with gorging jaws,
Shall wring from industry the food;

Nor fiery bigot's holy laws
Lay waste our fields and streets in blood!
—*Cho.*

Here strangers from a thousand shores,
Compelled by tyranny to roam,
Shall find, amidst abundant stores,
A nobler and a happier home.—*Cho.*

Here Art shall lift her laurel'd head,
Wealth, Industry and Peace divine;
And where dark, pathless forests spread,
Rich fields and lofty cities shine.—*Cho.*

LINCOLN AND LIBERTY

In 1860 the word "sucker" had not acquired its later meaning in slang, but meant a native of Illinois. Besides campaign songs, that election would be remembered for sharp national divisions.

Hurrah for the choice of the nation!
Our chieftain so brave and so true;
We'll go for the great reformation,
For Lincoln and Liberty too.
We'll go for the Son of Kentucky,
The hero of Hoosierdom through;
The pride of the Suckers so lucky,
For Lincoln and Liberty too.

They'll find what by felling and mauling,
Our rail-maker statesman can do;
For the people are everywhere calling
For Lincoln and Liberty too.
Then up with our banner so glorious,
The star-spangled red, white and blue,
We'll fight till our banner is victorious,
For Lincoln and Liberty too.

OLD ABE LINCOLN CAME OUT OF THE WILDERNESS

To the tune of "The Old Gray Mare" another campaign song of 1860 recommended the then unknown, virtually "dark horse" candidate from Illinois.

Old Abe Lincoln came out of the wilderness,
Out of the wilderness, out of the wilderness,

Old Abe Lincoln came out of the wilderness,
Down in Illinois.

THE INDEPENDENT FARMER

Long courted by all candidates, and identified with the announced program of any party seeking power, the independent farmer of today may well consider this old song a satire; yet political caution can still consider farm subsidies ahead of urban problems. G. F. Root and W. W. Fosdick wrote the song.

Let sailors sing of oceans deep,
Let soldiers praise their armor.
But in my heart this toast I'll keep:
The Independent Farmer.

He cares not how the world may move,
No doubts or fears confound him.
His little flock is linked in love
As household angels round him.

The gray old barn whose doors enfold
His ample store in measure
More rich in heaps of hoarded gold,
A precious, blessed treasure.

Chorus: He loves his country and his friends,
His honesty's his armor.
He's nature's nobleman in life,
The Independent Farmer.
(repeat last two lines)

THE SIDEWALKS OF NEW YORK

Although the population shift was well under way, this very urban song was no help to Al Smith, and may have done as much as religious prejudice to defeat him. Written in 1894 by Charles B. Lawlor and James W. Blake.

East Side, West Side, all around the town,
The tots sang "Ring a-Rosie," "London Bridge Is Falling Down."
Boys and girls together, me and Mamie O'Rourk,
Tripped the light fantastic on the sidewalks of New York.

OH! SUSANNA

Though seeming a natural for Alabama candidates, this Stephen Foster song in Negro dialect was never their choice; instead it became a GOP selection, but too early to win the southern vote.

I come from Alabama wid my banjo on my knee,
I'se gwan to Lou'siana, my true lub for to see.
It rained all night de day I left, de wedder it was dry;
The sun so hot, I froze to def; Susanna, don't you cry.

Oh! Susanna, do not cry for me,
I come from Alabama, wid my banjo on my knee.

I had a dream de udder night, when ebryt'ing was still;
I thought I saw Susanna dear, a-coming down de hill.
The buckwheat cake was in her mouf, de tear was in her eye,
Says I, I'se coming from de Souf, Susanna, don't you cry.

I soon will be in New Orleans, and den I'll look all 'round,
And when I find Susanna, I'll fall upon de ground.
But if I do not find her, then I'll surely die,
And when I'm dead and buried, Susanna, don't you cry.

THE DODGER SONG

In a series of verses dealing with the lawyer, the merchant, the farmer, and others, this folk song from the Arkansas hill country indicts the candidate too. Author and composer are unrecorded.

Oh, the candidate's a dodger,
Yes, a well known dodger.

Yes, the candidate's a dodger,
Yes, and I'm a dodger too.
He'll meet you and treat you
And ask you for your vote,
But look out, boys,
He's a-dodging for a note.

Refrain:
Yes, we're all dodging, a-dodging, dodging,
dodging,
Yes, we're all dodging out a way through the
world.

Oh, the lawyer he's a dodger,
Yes, a well known dodger,

Oh, the lawyer he's a dodger,
Yes, and I'm a dodger, too.
He'll plead your case and
Claim you for a friend,
But look out, boys, he's easy
For to bend!—*Ref.*

Oh, the merchant he's a dodger,
Yes, a well known dodger,
Oh, the merchant he's a dodger,
Yes, and I'm a dodger, too.
He'll sell you goods at double the price,
But when you go to pay him,
You'll have to pay him twice!—*Ref.*

Oh, the farmer he's a dodger,
Yes, a well known dodger,
Oh, the farmer he's a dodger,
Yes, and I'm a dodger, too.
He'll plow his cotton, he'll hoe his corn,
But he'll make a living just
As sure as you're born!—*Ref.*

Oh, the lover he's a dodger,
Yes, a well known dodger,
Oh, the lover he's a dodger,
Yes, and I'm a dodger, too.
He'll hug you and kiss you, and call you his
  bride,
But look out, girls, he's telling
You a lie!—*Ref.*

HOLD THE FORT FOR PROHIBITION

Although minority candidates as diverse as the two Wallaces, Henry and George, have likened the two big parties to Tweedledum and Tweedledee, it is an axiom of American politics that third parties can't win. But they add interest and uncertainty to elections, and long before the "noble experiment" of World War I, the Prohibition Party sought public support. Its many songs, in a songbook of the nineties, were mainly written to hymn tunes, as was the labor song also called "Hold the Fort."

Hark! Ye voters, hear the bugle
Calling to the fray:
"Prohibition" is our watchword,
Right shall win the day.

Chorus:
Storm the fort for Prohibition,
Captives signal still.
Answer back to their petition,
"By our votes we will."

See the haughty rumshop's banner
On the fortress wall;
Hurl the temp'rance ballots 'gainst it
Till the ramparts fall.—*Cho.*

Face the grogshop's bold defiance,
Never fear or fail;
Coward foes will soon surrender,
Voters do not quail.—*Cho.*

Round the temp'rance standard rally,
Friends of humankind.

Save the devotees of folly,
Wretched, poor and blind.—*Cho.*

Ho! my comrades, see our banner
Waving in the sky.
Hear our rallying hosanna
Echoing on high!—*Cho.*

All our land the foe engages!
Let no freeman lag!
See, the battle fiercely rages,
Rally round the flag!—*Cho.*

By the God who Freedom gave us
With immortal souls
Crush the foe who dares enslave us—
Forward to the polls!

Last chorus:
Hold the fort for Prohibition,
Freedom signals still.
Answer back to her petition,
"By our votes we will."

THE RED FLAG

The official song of the British Labour Party, sung in Parliament to celebrate a Labour victory, this was written by an Irish journalist, Jim Connell, for the London dock strike of 1889. The tune is that old favorite known to Germany as "Tannenbaum" and to Americans as "Maryland, My Maryland."

The people's flag is deepest red,
It shrouded oft our martyred dead,
And ere their limbs grew stiff and cold
Their hearts' blood dyed its ev'ry fold.

Chorus:
Then raise the scarlet standard high!
Within its shade we'll live or die.
Though cowards flinch and traitors sneer,
We'll keep the red flag flying here.

It waved above our infant might
When all ahead seemed dark as night;

It witnessed many a deed and vow:
We must not change its color now.

It well recalls the triumphs past;
It gives the hope of peace at last—
The banner bright, the symbol plain
Of human right and human gain.

With heads uncovered swear we all
To bear it onward till we fall.
Come dungeon dark or gallows grim,
This song shall be our parting hymn.

TAMMANY

Time-honored as one of the oldest of the unflattering characterizations of a political organization, this one written by Vincent Bryan and Gus Edwards was dedicated, tongue in cheek, to the Tammany boss of 1905.

Hiawatha was an Indian, so was Navajo.
Paleface organ grinders killed them many moons ago.
But there is a tribe of Indians that will never die.
When they're at the Indian club, this is their battle cry:

Chorus:
Tammany, Tammany,
Big Chief sits in his tepee,
Cheering braves to victory.
Tammany, Tammany,
Swamp 'em, swamp 'em, get the wampum, Tammany!

On the island of Manhattan, by the bitter sea
Lived this tribe of noble red men, tribe of Tammany.
From the Totem of the Green Light, wampum they would bring,
When their big Chief Man Behind would pass the pipe and sing:

Chorus:
Tammany, Tammany,
Stick together at the polls,
You'll have long green wampum rolls.
Tammany, Tammany,
Politicians get positions, Tammany!

When Reformers think it's time to show activity,
They blame everything that's bad on poor old Tammany.
All the farmers think that Tammany caused old Adam's fall,
They say when a bad man dies he goes to Tammany Hall.

Chorus:
Tammany, Tammany,
When a farmer's tax is due,
He puts all the blame on you.
Tammany, Tammany,
On the level you're a devil, Tammany.

HAPPY DAYS ARE HERE AGAIN

This cheerful number by Milton Ager was the reassuring anti-depression song of FDR's first term, his campaign song in the three succeeding terms, and a nostalgic reprise sung by his party in later years—even in Chicago, 1968. Copyright 1929 by Advanced Music Corporation. Used by permission of Warner Bros.–Seven Arts Music. All rights reserved.

Happy days are here again,   Let us sing a song of cheer again,
The skies above are clear again;   Happy days are here again!

WE STAND AT ARMAGEDDON

Theodore Roosevelt's Progressive Party picked up as its song theme an allusion from one of his speeches. There was no war on in 1912, but TR was no dove, even in peacetime. Copyright 1912 by C. R. Congden, director of singing, Progressive Convention.

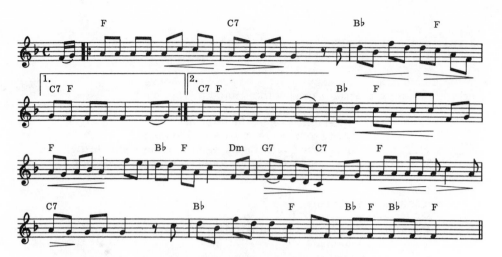

We stand at Armageddon and we battle for the Lord,
And all we ask to stead us is a blessing on each sword.
And tribes and factions mingle in one great fighting clan;
We issue forth to battle close behind a fighting man.

Then let the traitor tremble and the falterer go fawn—
We only ask to follow where the battle line is drawn.
And in the righteous conflict we pledge our sacred word—
We stand at Armageddon and we battle for the Lord.

Chorus:
We stand at Armageddon where fighting men have stood,
And creeds and races mingle in one common brotherhood.
And here, from day to darkness, we battle for the Lord;
Thy blessing, great Jehovah, grant on each impatient sword.

MR. ROOSEVELT, WON'T YOU PLEASE RUN AGAIN?

Written by Henry Myers, with music by Jay Gorney, this song celebrates FDR's precedent-shattering campaign for a third term, which carried every state except Maine and Vermont. Used by permission of author and composer.

In nineteen hundred and thirty-two
The banks were ruining me and you,
So what did he do?
He upped and closed the banks.
(He closed the banks, yes, he closed the banks.)
He saved us all and the banks besides.
He saved their money, he saved their hides,
He saved the bankers their banks,
But got no thanks.

Brother, sister, uncle, cousin, baby, father,
    mother,
All of us admit that two good terms deserve
    another.
Since they're pushing us down again,
He's started going to town again,
But not to save the banks!
To save us Yanks.

Mister Roosevelt, won't you please run again?
For we want you to do it,
You've got to go through it again.
Mister Roosevelt, won't you please run again?
For you're right in the middle

Of solving the riddle, and then
We're ready to march to the polls,
Ta-ra-ra boom-de-ay!
Ta-ra-ra-boom-de-ay! With a hullabaloo!

There'll be a brass band to welcome you
With a rum-ti-tid-dle-di on the drum,
A rum-ti-tid-dle-di-um-ti-tum.
A hundred million voters, here they come!
For you're the hope of all American women
    and men—
Mister Roosevelt, won't you do it again?

"My friends," he says—and friendship travels
    far—
Even foreign countries love the voice of F.D.R.
Does everyone know what they want? Yes!
Everyone knows what they want. Right!
History shows that everyone knows
Excepting Maine and Vermont!
If Hoover could last one term, then you are
    entitled to ten—
Mister Roosevelt, won't you please run again?

THE INVESTIGATOR'S SONG

Written by Harold Rome, this satirical comment on the Dies committee investigation of "Un-American activities" was first sung at Madison Square Garden by Zero Mostel. Later the song traveled even to England as a protest against the "witch hunting" of the Senate committee under Senator Joseph McCarthy. Copyright 1947 by Harold Rome. All rights reserved. Used by permission.

I've got a problem that is bothering me,
I've got a real unsolvable mystery.
It would stun G. K. Chesterton, foil Conan
 Doyle,
Drive Sherlock Holmes to the wall,
Stump Humphrey Bogart and Bacall.

Who's gonna investigate the man who investi-
 gates
The man who investigates me?
I don't doubt my loyalty,

But how about what his may be?
Who'll check the record of the man who
 checks the record
Of the man who checks the record of mine?
Seems to me there's gonna be an awfully long
 line.
One more problem puzzles me;
Pardon my strange whim:
But who's gonna investigate the man who in-
 vestigates
The man who investigates him?

Maybe they won't like the face he's wearing,
Maybe he'll have too much brass.
Maybe he's a guy who's fond of herring,
Maybe he drinks tea from a glass.
Believe me, brother, that won't pass.

Maybe they won't like the books he's reading,
Or the way he wants to pray.
Maybe he won't have the proper breeding;

Maybe he ran T.V.A.
Believe me, brother, that's out-ray.

Maybe he's the kind that does his own
    thinking,
Maybe he tries to use his head.
Maybe he goes in for vodka drinking;
Maybe his corpuscles are red.
Believe me, brother, off with his head.

I DON'T WANT YOUR MILLIONS, MISTER

To an old tune called "The Greenback Dollar," Jim Garland wrote this song for the Almanac Singers, explaining that Labor Party aims were a higher living standard rather than destruction of the American way. Copyright 1947 by People's Songs, Inc. Used by permission of present copyright holder, Sing Out!

I don't want your millions, mister;
I don't want your diamond ring.
All I want is the right to live, mister;
Give me back my job again.

I don't want your Rolls-Royce, mister;
I don't want your pleasure yacht;
All I want is food for my babies;
Give to me my old job back.

Take the two old parties, mister;
No difference in them I can see,
But with a Farmer-Labor party
We could set the people free.

THE BALLAD FOR UN-AMERICAN BLUES

A common saying of the alarmist period was that if you weren't called a Red, you really weren't doing much. This song summarizes that view. Words by Lee Hays and Walter Lowenfels; © *copyright 1947 by Sanga Music Inc. All rights reserved. Used by permission.*

I was down in St. James' Infirm'ry
So cold, so white, so bare.
They had me in a straitjacket,
And this is why I was there:

I've got me a million dollars
Also an oceangoing yacht;
Once I had me a pretty woman,
She swore she loved me for my character—as
    well as for my house and lot.

But my pretty woman has left me,
My everlasting woman has fled;
She said, "I'll not stay married
To a man that nobody calls a Red."

Well, you just ain't nobody at all
If nobody calls you Red.

You just ain't nobody at all,
You better hang your head.
You may be sweet sixteen, and never been
    kissed,
But nobody's gonna love you
If you ain't been called a Communist.
You ain't nobody at all
If nobody calls you Red.

Now, if you want to be successful
In the movies or the radio,
If you want to get ahead,
You got to be a Red,
'Cause J. Parnell Thomas says so.
Because you just ain't nobody at all,
If nobody calls you a Red.
If you go by what the papers say
There's one under eve'ry bed.

WHO? Well, let's see. There's Henry Wallace, Mrs. Roosevelt, Shirley Temple, teachers, preachers, movie actors, radio actors, Broadway playwrights, and that ain't all . . . ballad singers.

You ain't got no style
You ain't got no fame,
If the Un-America Committee hasn't scandalized your name, because
You ain't nobody at all
If nobody calls you a Red!

THE WISE MEN

Following the revolution in physics which ushered in the nuclear age, Malvina Reynolds issued a general indictment of mentally retarded politicians in this song, not really funny when the stakes are no longer wampum but the world. Copyright 1962 by Schroder Music Company, Berkeley, California. All rights reserved. Used by permission.

The wise men, the wise men, they do not know a thing;
They've gotten into leadership by tilting at the ring.
By wheeling, by dealing, by talking through their hat,
And when it comes to world affairs they're blind as a bat.

Chorus:
The wise men, the wise men, they'll finish us for sure.
The fools we can endure,
But heaven knows the cure
For the wisdom of the wise, wise men.

The wise men, the wise men, they give me a pain.
They don't know enough to come out of the rain.
The rain is filled with poison; it falls on good and ill.
If fallout doesn't get you, the firestorms will.—*Cho.*

Their words flow like a river, they dazzle in your eyes,
A prestidigitation of half-truths and lies;
Meanwhile the war machine goes rolling on and on:
The tapes will still be talking when everybody's gone.—*Cho.*

Your fate and my fate, the fate of all the lands
Are being wildly juggled in their butterfinger hands:
The lobby's there to nudge them to let something fall,
Down tumbles U.N., world peace and all.—*Cho.*

The wise men, the wise men, let's lock them in a room
And set them all to talking of megatons and doom,
And let them play at juggling maps and changing every border
And we won't let them out again 'til all the world's in order.—*Cho.*
Repeat first verse.

MISTER CONGRESSMAN

This interesting though perhaps overoptimistic threat to the men who under the constitutional balance of powers claim to represent the grass roots was written by Agnes (Sis) Cunningham, editor of Broadside, *to fit "Little Brown Jug." Copyright 1946 by Agnes Cunningham. Used by permission.*

Congressman, Mister Congressman,
Sitting down there in Washington,
You'd better listen to our song,
Or you ain't gonna be in Congress long.

Chorus:
No, no, no, no sirree,
In Washington you will not be.
You'd better listen to our song,
Or you ain't gonna be in Congress long.

Are you gonna listen to what we say,
Or let the big boys have their way?

Better get the people's point of view,
Or we're sure not a-gonna vote for you.—*Cho.*

The vets want work at decent pay,
And we don't mean three bucks a day;
So, see that there are jobs for all,
Or you'll be looking for a job next fall.—*Cho.*

Well, you know where the veteran lives,
Here and there with relatives.
If you think movin' around is fun,
We'll move you out of Washington.—*Cho.*

WHEN I WAS A LAD

Back to Gilbert and Sullivan, a famous song from Pinafore *with an unflattering analysis of political appointments had one immediate effect: Sullivan was knighted first.*

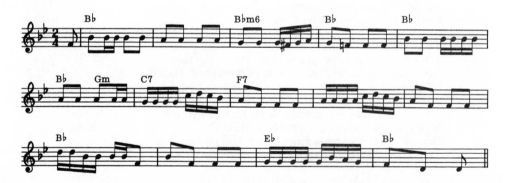

When I was a lad I served a term
As office boy to an attorney's firm,
I cleaned the windows and I swept the floor,
And I polished up the handle of the big front door.
I polished up that handle so carefulee,
That now I am the ruler of the Queen's Navee.

In serving writs I made such a name
That an articled clerk I soon became.

I wore clean collars and a brand-new suit
For the pass examination at the Institute.
That pass examination did so well for me
That now I am the ruler of the Queen's Navee.
(Repeat line.)

Of legal knowledge I acquired such a grip
That they took me into the partnership.
And that junior partnership, I ween,

Was the only ship that I ever had seen.
But that kind of ship so suited me
That now I am the ruler of the Queen's Navee.
(Repeat line.)

I grew so rich that I was sent,
By a pocket borough into Parliament.
I always voted at my party's call
And I never thought of thinking for myself at all.
I thought so little, they rewarded me

By making me the ruler of the Queen's Navee.
(Repeat line.)

Now landsmen all, wherever you may be,
If you want to rise to the top of the tree,
If your soul isn't fastened to an office stool,
Be careful to be guided by this golden rule:
Stick close to your desks and never go to sea,
And you all may be rulers of the Queen's Navee!
(Repeat line.)

KEEP IN THE MIDDLE OF THE ROAD

A song designed to help slaves flee northward, this one offers counsel to politicians of any period, and warns of a crowd gathered at the big white gate.

Keep in the middle of the middle of the middle of the road,
In the middle of the middle of the road.
Keep in the middle of the road. *(Repeat.)*
They's a-wait, waitin', waitin', waitin', waitin' in a crowd,
Keep in the middle of the road.

I can see them standin' round the big white gate,
We must travel along before it gets too late.
For it ain't no use to sit down and wait,
Keep in the middle of the road.
Then, children, keep in the middle of the road,
Children, keep in the middle of the road. *(Repeat.)*

Don't you look to the right, don't you look to the left,
Just keep in the middle of the middle of the middle of the road,
In the middle of the road.

IX

SONGS OF EMPIRE

We have no songs from the days of the pharaohs or from the Roman Empire, but those from later periods serve to remind us that empires, the last stage of expanding nations, rise and fall. From the march written to celebrate Napoleon's adventure into Egypt to the music written by Sir Edward Elgar for Queen Victoria's jubilee, songs have furnished a stirring accompaniment to the rise of empires, as well as a counterpoint to the resistance songs of subject peoples. As history travels its cycles, the old English play song "We Are the Romans" comes true, and today's critics of colonial expansion quote Gibbon in support of their objections to empire's westward course.

When during the Boer War one British song boasted,

"We don't want to fight, but, by jingo if we do,
We've got the guns, we've got the men, we've got the money, too,"

another famous song offered criticism: though Kipling supported British colonial power in general, he wrote "Recessional" as a warning years before the sun really set. Indeed, it was written as a new power was rising in the West when American rule would replace Spanish decline in the Philippines, and another song, one of our war with Mexico, would supplant "jingo" with "gringo" as a name for the latest aspirant to empire status.

WE ARE THE ROMANS

This English play song, its origin so obscure that it seems almost that it might go back to the time it recalls, is a simple "cops and robbers" game dividing children into two camps. But consider the belligerence and the taunts.

Oh, yes, we will have two cups full,
For we are the Romans.

Oh, no, you won't have two cups full,
For we are the English soldiers!

You're always up in border wars,
But we are the Romans.

Oh, yes, we're up in border wars,
For we are the English soldiers.

PARTANT POUR LA SYRIE
(Leaving for Syria)

They always leave with flags flying, and Napoleon's campaign in Egypt was on the whole a success. The love story seems to have no hidden significance, beyond its promise of happiness to the valiant.

Ordered off to Syria,	Partant pour la Syrie
The handsome young Dunois	Le jeune et beau Dunois
Came to ask his Marie	Venant prier Marie
To bless his luck in war.	De bénir ses exploits.
"You are my queen of heaven,"	"Faites, reine immortelle,"
On leaving her, said he.	Lui dit-il en partant.
"He who loves the loveliest	"Que j'aime la plus belle
Must the bravest be."	Et sois le plus vaillant."

Firm in resolution	Il trace sur la pierre
To win and not to yield,	Le serment de l'honneur,
The orders of his leader	Et va suivre à la guerre
He followed in the field.	Le comte, son seigneur.
And risking death or wounding,	Au noble vœu fidèle,
He bravely did declare	Il dit en combattant:
"Love ever to the loveliest	"Amour à la plus belle,
And to the brave, the fair."	Honneur au plus vaillant."

Observing well such courage	"On lui doit la victoire,
The noble lord who led	Vraiment," dit le seigneur.
Devised a signal honor:	"Puisque tu fais ma gloire,
His daughter to be wed.	Je ferai ton bonheur.
"For Isabelle's the fairest,	De ma fille Isabelle
As all must know is true,	Sois l'époux à l'instant,
And you, my boy, the bravest,	Car elle est la plus belle
I'll trust the girl to you."	Et toi le plus vaillant."

But Dunois kept his promise	A l'autel de Marie
To wed the fair Marie,	Ils contractent tous deux
And to his pretty sweetheart	Cette union chérie
Was married faithfully.	Qui seule rend heureux.
His friends who saw them wedded	Chacun dans la chapelle
Said, "Ah, how fair is she—	Disait en les voyant:
But to decline the other,	"Amour à la plus belle,
How very brave is he!" *	Honneur au plus vaillant."

DEUTSCHLAND ÜBER ALLES
(Germany Above All)

The attitude behind this naïve slogan set off World War I, being further particularized in the "Hymn of Hate" against England. Suddenly German forces, which once served as mercenaries for Britain against the American colonies, became the all-conquering shock troops of World War I, and, inspired again by the "Horst Wessel Song," of World War II. Never did Plato's recommendation of martial music have a more obvious effect on a music-loving people. Here the accompaniment is adapted from Haydn's "Kaiser Quartet."

Deutschland, Deutschland, über alles,
Über alles in der Welt,
Wenn es stet zu Schutz und Trutze
Brüderlich zusammen hält,
Von der Maas bis an die Memel,
Von der Etsch bis an den Belt;
Deutschland, Deutschland, über alles,
Über alles in der Welt.

German folk above all others,
All the others in the world.
Joined as one for our protection,
Standing firm in unity
From the Maas up to the Memel,
From the Etsch up to the Belt,
German folk above all others,
All the others in the world.

RECESSIONAL

Even before the world wars, with the sun still shining on the British Empire, the poet of that empire, Rudyard Kipling, had misgivings. The poem that expressed them, set to music by Reginald de Koven, appeared in The Ladies' Home Journal *in 1898.*

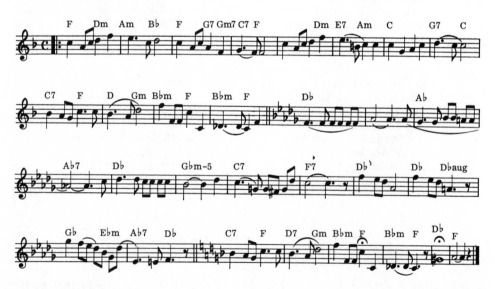

God of our fathers, known of old—
Lord of our far-flung battle line—
Beneath Whose awful hand we hold
Dominion over palm and pine—
Lord God of hosts, be with us yet,
Lest we forget—lest we forget!

The tumult and the shouting dies;
The captains and the kings depart:
Still stands Thine ancient sacrifice,
An humble and a contrite heart.
Lord God of hosts, be with us yet,
Lest we forget—lest we forget!

Far called, our navies melt away;
On dune and headland sinks the fire:
Lo, all our pomp of yesterday
Is one with Nineveh and Tyre!
Judge of the Nations, spare us yet,
Lest we forget—lest we forget!

If, drunk with sight of power, we loose
Wild tongues that have not Thee in awe—
Such boasting as the Gentiles use
Or lesser breeds without the Law—

Lord God of hosts, be with us yet,
Lest we forget—lest we forget!

Chorus:
For heathen heart that puts her trust
In reeking tube and iron shard—
All valiant dust that builds on dust,
And guarding, calls not Thee to guard—
For frantic boast and foolish word,
Thy mercy on Thy people, Lord!
Amen.

YE PARLIAMENTS OF ENGLAND

In a freedom song for the War of 1812, newly fledged America spoke up again —but note the last verse, second line, in which we proposed to annex Canada.

Ye parliaments of England, ye Lords and Commons, too,
Consider well what you're about, and what you're going to do.
You're now at war with Yankees, and I'm sure you'll rue the day
You roused the Sons of Liberty in North Americay.

You first confined our commerce; you said our ships shan't trade,
And then impressed our seamen, and used them as your slaves.
You then insulted Rodgers while sailing on the main,
And had we not declarèd war, you'd done it o'er again.

You thought our frigates were but few and Yankees could not fight,
Until brave Hull your *Guerrière* took and banished her from sight.
You're now at war with Yankees; I'm sure you'll rue the day
You roused the Sons of Liberty in North Americay.

Soon upon Lake Erie, bold Perry had his fun;
You own he beat your naval force and caused them all to run;
While Chauncey on Ontario, the like known ne'er before,
Your British squadron beat complete: some took, some run ashore.

Use every endeavor to try to cause a peace,
For Yankee ships are building fast, their navy to increase.
They will enforce their commerce; their laws by heaven were made,
That Yankee ships in time of peace in any port might trade.

Grant us free trade and commerce, don't you impress our men,
Give up all claims to Canada, then we'll make peace again.
Then, England, we'll respect you and treat you as a friend;
Respect our flag and citizens, then all these wars will end.

FREE AMERICAY

That recent wars mark a burgeoning of desire for dominion on the part of the United States is feared or deplored, as well as denied; and this song, with new verses by Joseph Warren for the Revolutionary War tune "The British Grenadiers," shows that, speaking for themselves, Americans were on record against conquest. But note the boast in the last verse.

That seat of science, Athens,
And earth's proud mistress, Rome;
Where now are all their glories?
We scarce can find a tomb.
Then guard your rights, Americans,
Nor stoop to lawless sway,
Oppose, oppose, oppose, oppose
For North Americay.

We led fair Franklin hither,
And, lo! the desert smiled;
A paradise of pleasure
Was opened to the world!
Your harvest, bold Americans,
No power shall snatch away!
Huzza, huzza, huzza, huzza
For free Americay.

Torn from a world of tyrants,
Beneath this western sky,
We formed a new dominion,
A land of liberty.
The world shall own we're masters here;
Then hasten on the day:
Huzza, huzza, huzza, huzza
For free Americay.

Proud Albion bowed to Cæsar,
And numerous lords before;
To Picts, to Danes, to Normans,
And many masters more;

But we can boast, Americans,
We've never fallen a prey;
Huzza, huzza, huzza, huzza
For free Americay.

God bless this maiden climate,
And through its vast domain
May hosts of heroes cluster,
Who scorn to wear a chain:
And blast the venal sycophant
That dares our rights betray;
Huzza, huzza, huzza, huzza
For free Americay.

Lift up your heads, ye heroes,
And swear with proud disdain
The wretch that would ensnare you
Shall lay his snares in vain;
Should Europe empty all her force,
We'll meet her in array,
And fight and shout, and shout and fight
For free Americay.

Some future day shall crown us
The masters of the main.
Our fleets shall speak in thunder
To England, France and Spain;
And the nations o'er the oceans spread
Shall tremble and obey
The sons, the sons, the sons, the sons
Of brave Americay.

GREEN GROW THE LILACS

The war with Mexico in 1846, over the annexation of Texas, took across the Rio Grande a song dating from the British border wars. The story goes that its first words, "Green grow," were made into the word "Gringo" by Mexicans seeking a name for the invaders.

He sings:
Oh, green grow the lilacs and so does the rue.
How sad's been the day since I parted from you.
But at our next meeting our love we'll renew;
We'll change the green lilacs for red, white and blue.

She sings:
I once had a sweetheart but now I have none,
He's gone off and left me to live here alone.
He's gone off and left me, contented to be.
He must love another girl better than me.

He sings:
I passed my love's window, both early and late,
The look that she gave me, it made my heart ache.
Oh, the look that she gave me was painful to see,
For she loves another one better than me.

She sings:
Green grow the lilacs, all sparkling with dew.
I'm lonely, my darling, since parting with you.
But by our next meeting I hope to prove true,
And change the green lilacs for the red, white and blue.

Both:
Oh, green grow the lilacs and so does the rue, etc

THE SAIGON CHILDREN

Malvina Reynolds' song comments on the effect of foreign occupation on the children whose homeland is a country known to their parents as French Indo-China. Copyright 1966 by Schroder Music Company. All rights reserved. Used by permission.

The French have gone and the Yanks have
    come,
Say the Saigon children.
We live in war like our natural home,
Say the Saigon children.

The Yankee comes when the French retreats,
Say the Saigon children,
We play the game of War in the Streets . . .

You smash and burn, smash and burn . . .
Viet kids are quick to learn . . .

"Seek and destroy! Seek and destroy!" . . .
What a line for a five-year-boy . . .

We needed rice and you gave us a stone . .
Stone in the hand is easy thrown . . .

Napalm burns through the forest cover . . .
A jeep will burn if you turn it over . . .

Take your PX and leave us alone,
Say the Saigon children.
Vietnam is our natural home,
Say the Saigon children.

HONOR OUR COMMITMENT

A phrase often employed by defenders of war policy based on the SEATO agreements arranged by the late John Foster Dulles is here considered. Words and music copyright 1965 by Jacqueline Sharpe. First published in Broadside.

Oh, gather round, you bully boys, and hear just what I say.
We have a Great Society in the good old U.S.A.
So listen, nations of the earth, we give our promise true,
If you don't obey your Uncle Sam, his troops will visit you.

Chorus:
And we'll honor our commitment, honor our commitment,
Even if the world goes up in the smoke of a mushroom cloud,
Honor our commitment, honor our commitment,
Get buried with our brothers in one great communal shroud.

Now, widows all like candy canes, and orphans all like jam,
And Band-Aids come in handy for the wounded in Vietnam,
So send your package out today to the homeless kids and wives,
We're sure the ones we haven't killed will love us all their lives.—*Cho.*

We're shocked to death at India, enraged at Pakistan,
So we've told Arthur Goldberg to denounce them, man to man.
There in the UN's sacred halls, we've raised a mighty fuss,
Cease Fire, we tell all nations—that means everyone but us.—*Cho.*

These Latin revolutions, now, we watch 'em like a hawk
And when we try to lend a hand we can't see why they squawk.
If only those Dominicans would follow in our track,
Then soldiers wouldn't feel obliged to shoot them in the back.—*Cho.*

THE FOUR RIVERS

*When TVA came to the Tennessee Valley, it was remarked that rivers know
nothing of state boundaries. The idea is extended to nations in this song written
by Henry Myers, with music by Jay Gorney. Sung by Paul Robeson. Reprinted
by permission of author and composer.*

Here's the story of the four rivers that the eyes of the world are on:
They're called the Thames, the Mississippi, and the Yangtze and the Don.
Oh, the four rivers, the four rivers, apart as they could be,
But they discovered how to get together when the rivers rolled down to the sea.
River rolling down to the open sea.

Here's the story of the four sailors that the eyes of the world are on:
Their names are John, and Mau and Tommy, and the fourth is named Ivan.
Oh, the four sailors, the four sailors, they raised them separately
But they discovered how to get together when the rivers rolled down to the sea,
River rolling down to the open sea.

Now the people of the four rivers must be friends as time rolls on,
Beside the Thames, the Mississippi, and the Yangtze and the Don.
The four rivers, the four rivers, wherever men may be
They must discover how to get together where the rivers roll down to the sea.
River rolling down to the open sea.

COPS OF THE WORLD

That world policing is the job of the UN, or not to be undertaken by any nation acting alone, is the conclusion of this song about unilateral efforts to restore order in distant lands. Words and music by Phil Ochs; copyright 1966 by Barricade Music, Inc. All rights reserved. Used by permission.

Come, get out of the way, boys,
Quick, get out of the way.
You'd better watch what you say, boys,
Better watch what you say.
We've rammed in your harbor, we've tied to your port,
And our pistols are hungry and our tempers are short.
So bring your daughters around to the fort
'Cause we're the cops of the world, boys,
    we're the cops of the world.

We pick and choose as we please, boys,
Pick and choose as we please.
You'd best get down on your knees, boys,
You'd best get down on your knees.
We're hairy and horny and ready to shack,
And we don't care if you're yellow or black,
Just take off your clothes and lay down on your back
'Cause we're the cops of the world, boys,
    we're the cops of the world.

Our boots are needing a shine, boys,
Our boots are needing a shine.
But our Coca-Cola is fine, boys,
Coca-Cola is fine.
We've got to protect all our citizens fair,
So we'll send a battalion for everyone there,
And maybe we'll leave in a couple of years
'Cause we're the cops of the world, boys,
    we're the cops of the world.

And clean the johns with a rag, boys,
Clean the johns with a rag.
If you like you can use your flag, boys,
If you like you can use your flag.
We've got too much money, we're looking for toys;
Guns will be guns and boys will be boys,
But we'll gladly pay for all we've destroyed
'Cause we're the cops of the world, boys,
    we're the cops of the world.

And please stay off of the grass, boys,
Please stay off of the grass;
Here's a kick in the ass, boys,
Here's a kick in the ass.
We'll smash down your doors; we don't bother to knock;
We've done it before so why all the shock;
We're the biggest and toughest kids on the block
'Cause we're the cops of the world, boys,
    we're the cops of the world.

And when we've butchered your sons, boys,
When we've butchered your sons,
Have a stick of our gum, boys,
Have a stick of our bubblegum.
We own half the world, oh say can you see,
And the name of our profits is Democracy,
So like it or not you will have to be free
'Cause we're the cops of the world, boys,
    we're the cops of the world.

X

SONGS FOR PEACE

Peace, warned Bernard Shaw, was not to be established by Christmas cards; but the genuine concern for peace shown by ordinary citizens in today's world is surely the most hopeful aspect of the nuclear age. Along with the comment that no good songs were written for our Korean and Vietnam wars, there is in this country a phenomenal outpouring of peace songs of every description and degree of fervor. The Civil War produced one, "When This Cruel War Is Over," and World War I another, "I Didn't Raise My Boy to Be a Soldier," while the peaceful sentiments of Negroes were expressed by the spiritual "Ain't Gwine Study War No More." Only the last of these three can fairly be included in this book; the first is debatable because, although the cruelty of war is now admitted, any southerner will argue that the Civil War reprisals, backlashes, and prejudices are still with us. The second, at the time, was buried under parodies such as "I Didn't Raise My Boy to Be a Slacker" and "I Didn't Raise My Dog to Be a Sausage."

Today's songs, expressing a new urgency proper to the atomic age, have a wider circulation and a better hearing.

MRS. McGRATH

"When there's no fighting, there's Ireland no more—" but even while Irishmen were policing the world for the British, this song is evidence of opposition to the practice.

Oh, Mrs. McGrath, the sergeant said,
Would you like to make a soldier out of your son Ted?
With a scarlet coat and a big cocked hat;
Now, Mrs. McGrath, wouldn't you like that?

Chorus:
Wid yer too-ri-a, fold-the-diddle-a, too-ri-oo-ri, oo-ri-a. *(Repeat.)*

So Mrs. McGrath lived on the seashore
For the space of seven long years or more,
Till she saw a big ship sailing into the bay,
"Hello, hello, I think tis he.—*Cho.*

"Oh, Captain dear, where have you been?
Have you been sailing on the Mediterraneen?
Oh, have you any tidings of my son Ted
Is the poor boy living or is he dead?"—*Cho.*

Then up comes Ted without any legs
And in their place two wooden pegs.
She kissed him a dozen times or two,
Saying, "Holy Moses, it isn't you.—*Cho.*

"Oh, Teddy me boy," the widow cried,
"Your two fine legs were your mama's pride.
I'd rather have my son as he used to be,
Than the King of France and his whole navee.
—*Cho.*

"Oh, then were you drunk or were you blind
That you left your two fine legs behind?
Or was it walkin' upon the sea
Wore your two fine legs from the knees away?
—*Cho.*

"All foreign wars I do proclaim,
Between Don John and the King of Spain.
By the heavens I'll make them rue the time,
They swept the legs from a child of mine."
—*Cho.*

FORWARD ALL YE FAITHFUL

In the nineties another Sullivan, Arthur W. Sullivan of New York, wrote a new lyric for his English namesake's famous hymn, "Onward, Christian Soldiers." Published in an educational magazine but not widely known, this one is interesting as an early expression of the peace movement in this country. Included here is "Christians at War," a satiric parody from the old IWW songbook.

Forward all ye faithful, seeking love and peace,
Hast'ning on the era when all strife shall cease.
All the saintly sages lead us in the way—
Forward in their footsteps toward that perfect day.

Chorus:
Forward all ye faithful,
Seeking love and peace,
Hast'ning on the era
When all strife shall cease.

Raise the voice of triumph, "Peace on earth, goodwill."
Angels sang this anthem, let us sing it still.
War's foundations quiver at this song of peace—
Brothers, let us sing it till all strife shall cease.—*Cho.*

Wealth and power shall perish, nations rise and wane,
Love of others only, steadfast shall remain.
Hate and greed can never 'gainst this love prevail—
It shall stand triumphant when all else shall fail.—*Cho.*

Parody: "Christians at War"
Onward, Christian soldiers! Duty's way is plain:
Slay your Christian neighbors, or by them be slain.
Pulpiteers are spouting effervescent swill,
God above is calling you to rob and rape and kill.
All your acts are sanctified by the Lamb on high—
If you love the Holy Ghost, go murder, pray and die.

Onward, Christian soldiers, rip and tear and smite!
Let the gentle Jesus bless your dynamite.
Splinter skulls with shrapnel, fertilize the sod.
Folks who do not speak your tongue deserve the curse of God. . . .
Burn the peasants' cottages, orphans leave bereft—
In Jehovah's holy name, wreak ruin right and left.

Onward, Christian soldiers! Drench the land with gore;
Mercy is a weakness all the gods abhor.
Bayonet the babies, jab the mothers too;

Hoist the cross of Calvary to hallow all you do.
File your bullets' noses flat, poison every well;
God decrees your enemies must all go plumb to hell.

SHALOM, CHAVERIM (Peace, Fellowmen)

A traditional Hebrew round, with lyric by Paul Campbell, recalls a saying familiar to all men of goodwill. Copyright 1951 by Folkways Music Publishers, Inc. International copyright secured. All rights reserved. Used by permission.

Shalom, chaverim, shalom, chaverim,
Shalom, shalom,
L' hit raot, l' hit raot,
Shalom, shalom.

Glad tidings we bring of peace on earth,
Goodwill toward men,
Of peace on earth,
Good will toward men. *(Repeat.)*

THE WAR IS OVER (La Guerre Est Finie)

With an English version by Lee Hays and music by Ruth Berns, this old French song might well be contemporary. Copyright 1967 by Sanga Music, Inc., 200 West Fifty-seventh Street, New York. All rights reserved. Used by permission.

The war is over for many thousand gone,
Peace forever for many thousand gone,
The end of pain and fear,
The end of all desire,
The end of pride and glory,
All vanished in the fire.

The war is over for many thousand gone,
The war is over.
The war goes on.

La guerre est finie pour les milliers partis,
La paix éternelle pour les milliers partis,
La fin de la peine et la peur,
Et la fin de tout désir,
Le fin de l'orgeuil et de la gloire,
Tout étient dans le feu.
La guerre est finie pour les milliers partis.
La guerre est finie.
La guerre, elle suit.

WE DIDN'T KNOW

A peace song that probes for the cause of war in supposedly civilized countries, this one by Tom Paxton dramatizes the national crimes of apathy and ignorance that add up to common guilt. Copyright 1965 by Deep Fork Music, Inc. All rights reserved. Used by permission.

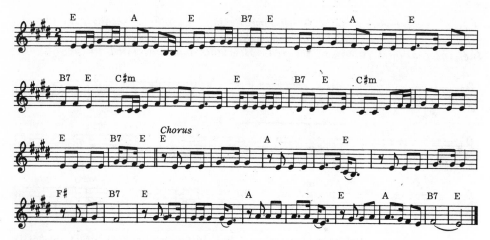

"We didn't know," said the burgomeister, "about the camps on the edge of town.
It was Hitler and his crew that tore the German nation down.
We saw the cattle cars, it's true, and maybe they carried a Jew or two,
They woke us up as they rattled through—
But what did you expect me to do?
We didn't know at all, we didn't see a thing;
You can't hold us to blame—what could we do?
It was a terrible shame,
But we can't bear the blame—
Oh, no, not us—we didn't know."

"We didn't know," said the congregation,
Singing a hymn in their church of white.
"The press was full of lies about us,
Preacher told us we were right.
The outside agitators came,
They burned some churches and put the blame
On decent southern people's names,
To set our colored people aflame,
And maybe some of our boys got hot
And a couple of niggers and Reds got shot.
They should have stayed where they belong
And preacher would've told us if we'd done wrong."

"We didn't know," said the puzzled voter,
Watching the President on TV.
"I guess we've got to drop those bombs
If we're gonna keep South Asia free.
The President's such a peaceful man,
I guess he's got some kind of plan,
They say we're torturing prisoners of war,
But I don't believe that stuff no more,
Torturing prisoners is a Communist game
And you can bet they're doing the same.
I wish this war was over and through,
But what do you expect me to do?"

PEACE SONG

Pablo Neruda wrote the Spanish lyrics; Bertold Brecht translated into German; and Eric Bentley wrote the English lyric to music by Hanns Eisler. Published by both Broadside *and* Sing Out! *Used by permission.*

Peace to the house that is your house,
Peace to the house that is mine.
Peace to the peaceful neighbor,
Peace to both mine and thine.
Peace to Korean children,
Peace to workers on the Ruhr;

Peace to New York truck drivers,
Peace to coolies in Singapore.
Peace to the men, to the women,
Peace to the old, to the small.
Peace to the land, to the ocean,
That they may serve us all.

THAT BOMB HAS GOT TO GO

When the English staged their protest march from Aldermaston to London, Peggy Seeger and Ewan MacColl wrote this song to the tune of an old sea chantey. Copyright 1963 by Stormking Music. All rights reserved. Used by permission.

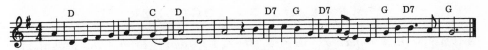

We're marching to Trafalgar Square,
Oh, yes, Oh!
Today we're marching to declare,
That bomb has got to go.

Chorus:
That bomb it weighs a ton or so,
Oh, yes, Oh!
Can kill a million at one go,
That bomb has got to go!

Oh, dropping bombs is all the rage,
But I'd rather live to a ripe old age.—*Cho.*

Fallout here and fallout there,
And Strontium Ninety everywhere.—*Cho.*

This overcrowded world is small,
But it's better than no world at all.—*Cho.*

I had a dream the other night;
I dreamed the Tories saw the light.—*Cho.*

THE H-BOMBS' THUNDER

Also for the Aldermaston marchers, John Brunner wrote new words for an old hymn tune—borrowed earlier by union miners—which he, John Hasted, and Eric Winter changed for the occasion. Copyright 1958 by John Brunner, copyright assigned 1966 to Brunner Fact & Fiction Ltd. Used by permission.

Don't you hear the H-Bombs' thunder,
Echo like the crack of doom?
While they rend the skies asunder,
Fallout makes the world a tomb.
Do you want your homes to tumble,
Rise in smoke towards the sky?

Will you let your cities crumble,
Will you see your children die?
Men and women stand together,
Do not heed the men of war.
Make your minds up now or never,
Ban the Bomb forevermore.

WE'LL ALL GO TOGETHER

Another Scottish objection, sung to "She'll Be Comin' Round the Mountain," echoes the fears of the atomic scientists and the warnings of nuclear-age films that "It'll all be accidental when it comes."

Oh, we'll all go together when it comes,
            (Repeat.)
Yes, we'll all go together,
However nice the weather,
Yes, we'll all go together when it comes.

It'll all be accidental when it comes, *(Repeat.)*
It'll all be accidental,
Just that some poor guy went mental,
It'll all be accidental when it comes.

It'll be too late to stop it when it comes,
            (Repeat.)
It'll be too late to stop it,
When we're just about to cop it,
It'll be too late to stop it when it comes.

So, let's stop it now before it comes, *(Repeat.)*
Yes, let's stop it now,
Make a devil of a row,
Let's stop it now before it comes.

NO HIDING PLACE

American Negroes didn't need to write new songs about the bomb. They had this good prophetic one from way back, and they added new words to "We Shall Not Be Moved."

There's no hiding place down there,
No hiding place down there.
Hallelujah, brother—
No hiding place down there.
(Praise the Lord!)

Oh, I went to the rocks to hide my face,
The rock cried out,
No hiding place!
There's no hiding place down there.

BAN, BAN, BAN THE BLOODY H-BOMB

Of all the English ban-the-bomb songs, this is perhaps the most emphatic, with its very British profanity and understatement of patriotic sentiment. The tune is "Glory Hallelujah" and the lyric is by Alex Comfort. Used by permission.

To hell with all the humbug and
To hell with all the lies,
To hell with all the strontium
Continuing to rise.
To hell with all the Charlies
With a gift for compromise,
If they won't ban the H-Bomb now!

Chorus:
Ban, ban, ban the bloody H-Bomb *(3 times)*
If you want to stay alive next year!

We're going to stop the loonies
And preserve the human race,
We're going to save our country

'Cause we love the dear old place,
We might have to stuff a rocket
Up the rocket builders' base—
But we're going to ban the H-Bomb now.
                                    —*Cho.*

Somewhere in the States they've
Got a button painted red,
If anybody sits on it we'll
All of us be dead,
Meanwhile a million children
Are waiting to be fed
So we're going to ban the H-Bomb now.—*Cho.*

TALKING ATOMIC BLUES

Though this explanation of atomic power by Vern Partlow is an early one, it is one of the clearest. Copyright 1950 by Bibo Music Publishers, Inc. Used by permission.

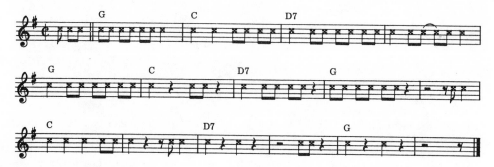

I'm gonna preach you all a sermon 'bout
    Old Man Atom,
And I don't mean the Adam in the Bible
    datum.
I don't mean the Adam Mother Eve mated,
I mean the thing that science liberated.
You know Einstein said he was scared,
And if he's scared, brother, I'm scared.

Yes, life used to be such a simple joy.
The cyclotron was a supertoy,
Folks got born, they'd work and marry,
And "atom" was a word in the dictionary;
And then it happened. . . .

These science guys, from every clime
They all pitched in with overtime.
Before you knew it, the job was done;
They'd hitched up the power of the doggone
    sun,
Splitting atoms, right and left,
While the diplomats . . .
Were splitting hairs . . .

Then the cartel crowd up and put on a show,
They're gonna turn back the clock on the
    UNO.
Grab a corner on atoms and maybe extinguish
Every damn atom that can't speak English.
Down with foreign-born atoms!
America for American atoms!
Step right up, folks, and let's atomize world
    peace. . . .

Ah, but the atom's international, in spite of
    hysteria.
Flourishes in Utah, also in Siberia.
He don't care about politics
Or who got what into whichever fix.
All he wants to do is sit around . . .
And have his nucleus bombarded by neutrons.

Yes, it's up to the people; the atom don't care.
You can't fence him in; he's just like air.
And whether you're white, black, red or
    brown,
The question is this, when you boil it down,
To be or not to be!
That is the question. . . .

And the answer to it all ain't military datum,
Like "Who gets there fustest with the mostest
    atoms,"
But the people of the world must decide their
    fate,
We got to stick together or disintegrate.
We hold these truths to be self-evident:
All men
Could be cremated equal.

WALK IN PEACE

The difficult path to peace was charted as early as 1946 by the calypso singer Sir Lancelot Pinard. Copyright 1946 by Sir Lancelot Pinard. Used by permission.

Everyone who's been to school
Heard about the Golden Rule.
It's a story old but true,
Do unto others as you'd have them do unto
    you.
Now, the way it looks to me,
It's a case of reciprocity;
We must observe it implicitly
If we hope to save the world from calamity.

Chorus:
For it's as simple as one and one make two,
Do unto others as you'd have them do unto
    you,
It's the only way that wars will cease,
And men of goodwill shall walk in peace.

We must learn to give and take,
If a better world we hope to make.
How can you teach Hungarians democracy,
While at home you practice racial bigotry?
We must get the other fellow's point of view;
He has a right to his opinions, too.
You know, the "know-how" of being free
Is not a Yankee monopoly.

Chorus:
For it's as simple as one and one make two,
Do unto others as you'd have them do unto
    you,
It's the only way that wars will cease,
And men of goodwill shall walk in peace.

We condemn Russians for tyranny,
And denial to the press of liberty.
But tell me this one thing, candidly:
Is Greece or Spain, or even China, free?
And black men in this great democracy,
Do they walk with noble dignity?
Or do they hang their heads in shame,
And torture their souls in a Jim Crow train?

Chorus:
For it's as simple as one and one make two,
Do unto others as you'd have them do unto
    you,
It's the only way that wars will cease,
And men of goodwill shall walk in peace.

What a pity it is to see
Churches in our beloved country
Denying the brotherhood of man
By bowing to the doctrine of segregation.
We must practice what we preach,
If we would Poles and Balkans teach,
That in our great land the world might see
A shining example of democracy.—*Cho.*

TAKE BACK YOUR ATOM BOMB

The first Americans joined the British in A-bomb protest. Peter La Farge wrote many good songs for his friends the Indians, but none more telling than this reproach to the nuclear age, which he sang for the Folkways album "As Long As the Grass Shall Grow." Used by permission.

Take back your fallout
Give us back the bow;
You whites are always in a hurry,
But we don't want to go.

Chorus:
Take back your atom bomb
Give us back the arrow
God's eye is on the neutron
As well as on the sparrow.

Take back your heavy rains,
Give us back the sky;
We liked it clean;
We don't want to say good-bye.—*Cho.*

Take back the megaton,
Give us back our lances;
We will make our own wars
And we will dance our dances.—*Cho.*

WHAT HAVE THEY DONE TO THE RAIN?

Joan Baez hailed this as the gentlest of peace songs, but since the test ban it can claim some success, along with other complaints, in changing world policy. Music and words by Malvina Reynolds. Copyright 1962 by Schroder Music Company, Berkeley, California. All rights reserved. Used by permission.

Just a little rain, falling all around,
The grass lifts its head to the heavenly sound,
Just a little rain,
Just a little rain,
What have they done to the rain?

Just a little boy, standing in the rain,
The gentle rain that falls for years.
And the grass is gone,
The boy disappears,

And rain keeps falling
Like helpless tears—
And what have they done to the rain?

Just a little breeze out of the sky,
The leaves pat their hands as the breeze
    blows by,
Just a little breeze
With some smoke in its eye—
What have they done to the rain?

CIVIL DEFENSE SIGN

Here objection to the take-cover program may have done its bit to silence the sirens. Will they come back again with "anti-missile missiles?" Music and lyric copyright 1965 by Appleseed Music, Inc. All rights reserved. Used by permission.

Chorus:
When you see this sign it's time to go—
This sign, this sign.
You'll know it's time to go when the siren
 starts to blow,
Remember the Civil Defense sign.

This sign won't save you and me,
This sign, this sign.
But it's a hole for the souls of your friends
 and mine,
Remember the Civil Defense sign.

My town's got more signs than yours,
More signs, more signs.
I've got more Band-Aids, more ice cubes and
 more iodine,
Just in case it hurts some friends of mine.

I won't be the one to die,
To die, to die.
Of course a certain percentage just has to go
But I won't be the one to die.

Make the missiles so Daddy will have a job,
A job, a job.
When the missiles start to fly we can all lie
 down and die,
Then Daddy won't have to work any more.

WAY OF THE DINOSAUR

Speaking for the younger generation, Bill Frederick wrote both words and music to prove the established order dangerously dated. First published in Broadside. *Copyright 1964 by Bill Frederick. Used by permission.*

Puff the Magic Dragon used to live by the sea.
But the sea dried up, and the weather changed, and along came you and me.
We took the place of the dying race because we knew the score,
And Puff the Magic Dragon went the way of the Dinosaur.

Chorus:
Dinosaur's outdated, he don't live here anymore.
The good old days are goin' the way of the Dinosaur.

All throughout the ages people lived in slavery.
Then came the revolution; now we fight for liberty.
The day is done when we would run or cower on the floor.
Uncle Tom's already gone the way of the Dinosaur.—*Cho.*

In every day, some people say that people never change.
You can't change that old status quo, but don't you think it's strange?
The Dinosaur said the same damn thing, and he's not here anymore.
Them that can't change peacefully go the way of the Dinosaur.—*Cho.*

People starving everywhere, we got silos full of grain.
People dying everywhere, we got medicine and brains.
People crying everywhere, we got missiles ready for war.
We're all dried up and fossilized, the way of the Dinosaur.—*Cho.*

There's time to start a-changin' 'fore the world can pass us by.
There's time to feed a hungry world before the missiles fly.
There's time to build a new world, put an end to hate and war.
There's time to think before we're extinct, the way of the Dinosaur.—*Cho.*

Chorus:
Dinosaur's outdated, he don't live here anymore.
The good old days are goin' the way of the Dinosaur.

TWENTY TONS OF T.N.T.

This frightening bit of fact-finding and arithmetic was written and sung to Broadway audiences by the talented British star Michael Flanders. Copyright 1967 by Michael Flanders. All rights reserved. Used by permission of Mesquite Music Corp., New York.

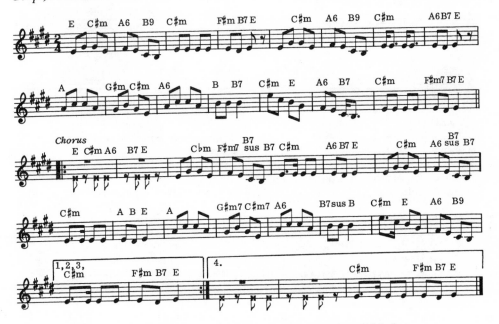

I have seen it estimated, somewhere between death and birth,
There are now three thousand million people living on this earth.
And the stockpiled mass destruction of the nuclear pow'rs that be
Equals for each man or woman TWENTY TONS OF T.N.T.

Chorus:
Twenty tons of T.N.T.?
TWENTY TONS OF T.N.T.

Ev'ry man of ev'ry nation shall receive this allocation,
Texan, Bantu, Slav, or Maori, Argentine or Singhalee,
Ev'ry maiden brings this dowry: TWENTY TONS OF T.N.T.—*Cho.*

Not for thirty silver shilling—twenty thousand pounds a killing,
Twenty hundred years of teaching give to each his legacy:
Plato, Buddha, Christ or Lenin, TWENTY TONS OF T.N.T.—*Cho.*

Father, mother, son and daughter, "Give us land and seed and water,"
Children have no need for sharing. At each new nativity
Come the ghostly Magi bearing TWENTY TONS OF T.N.T.—*Cho.*

Ends the tale that has no sequel, now in death are all men equal.
Teach me how to love my neighbor, do to him as he to me—
Share the fruits of all our labor: TWENTY TONS OF T.N.T.—*Cho.*

PEACE ISN'T TREASON

Do the bystanders yell accusations at peace marchers? Here's the answer, by Malvina Reynolds. Copyright 1967 by Schroder Music Company, Berkeley, California. All rights reserved. Used by permission.

Chorus:

Peace isn't treason,
Peace is good reason,
Peace is Heaven's will.
"Peace on earth!" is what He said,
And I believe it still.

Wars there have always been,
We walk the same old way,
We walk the road our fathers went
When they have gone astray,
When they have gone astray.—*Cho.*

Though the voice of reason speaks,
Unreasoned voices rage,
And so we add another line
To history's bloody page,
History's bloody page.—*Cho.*

We must learn to live with peace
And take it as our friend,
We must learn to live with peace,
Or all the world will end,
All the world will end.—*Cho.*

IF YOU LOVE YOUR UNCLE SAM
(Bring Them Home)

When support for our boys is demanded, don't just pay taxes and send candy and cigarettes; bring them home, says Pete Seeger. Copyright 1968 by Stormking Music, Inc. All rights reserved. Used by permission.

If you love your Uncle Sam,
Ref: Bring them home, bring them home.
Support our boys in Vietnam—
Ref: Bring them home, bring them home.

It'll make our generals sad, I know *(Ref.)*
They want to tangle with the foe. *(Ref.)*

They want to test their weaponry *(Ref.)*
But here is their big fallacy: *(Ref.)*

Our foe is hunger and ignorance, *(Ref.)*
You can't beat them with bombs and guns.
(Ref.

may be right, I may be wrong! *(Ref.)*
But I got a right to sing this song. *(Ref.)*

Now you may think I'm a pacifist, *(Ref.)*
But that's not true, I must confess. *(Ref.)*

If an army invaded this land of mine, *(Ref.)*
You'd find me out on the firing line, *(Ref.)*

Even if they brought their planes to bomb,
(Ref.)
Though they brought helicopters and napalm.
(Ref.)

Show these generals their fallacy; *(Ref.)*
They don't have the right weaponry. *(Ref.)*

For defense you need common sense; *(Ref.)*
They don't have the right armaments. *(Ref.)*

The world needs teachers, books and schools,
(Ref.)
And learning a few universal rules. *(Ref.)*

So if you love your Uncle Sam *(Ref.)*
Support our men in Vietnam. *(Ref.)*

PLAYING WAR

You don't grow up to kill if you don't start with tin swords and toy drums, or let's hope not, says Malvina Reynolds. Copyright 1964 by Schroder Music Company, Berkeley, California. All rights reserved. Used by permission.

There's a nameless war in Vietnam,
There's wars in many lands,
And my little boy in our back yard
Has a toy gun in his hands,
And the big toymakers in Buffalo
Are getting my boy set to go,
But I say No and the kids say No,
We're playing war no more.

Today it's a plastic tank or plane,
Tomorrow it's for real;
Today it shoots a wooden shot,
Tomorrow the bullet's steel.
And the buyers in the department store
Are getting my boy ready for war,
But I say No and the kids say No,
We're playing war no more.

Well, a little red wagon on the hill
Can pull his pal along,
But we want no little revolver gun
To shoot his buddy down.

The factories run in old New York
To get him ready for the dirty work,
But I say No and the kids say No,
We're playing war no more.

There's many a boy like my own boy
Who's lying in the mud,
And his good young life was cut away
While it was in the bud.
So the stores that offer death for play
Will have to get rich some other way,
Cause I say No and the kids say No,
We're playing war no more.

Well, the Army brass and the C.I.A.
Are hardly grown-up boys,
And they're playing now with atom bombs
As though they were plastic toys.
But the life of the world is on the throw,
And while there is time, we're shouting "No!"
We say No and the kids say No,
We're playing war no more.

I AIN'T MARCHIN' ANY MORE

Phil Ochs offers in this one a fascinating résumé of the past, with conclusions from that experience. Copyright 1964 by Appleseed Music, Inc. All rights reserved. Used by permission.

Oh, I marched to the Battle of New Orleans
At the end of the early British war
A young land started growin', the young
  blood started flowin',
But I ain't marchin' any more.

Interlude:
It's always the old to lead us to the war,
Always the young to fall.
Now look at all we won with a sabre and a
  gun—
Tell me, was it worth it all?

For I killed my share of Injuns in a thousand
  different fights,
I was there at the Little Big Horn;
I heard many men a-lyin',
I saw many more a-dyin',
And I ain't marchin' any more.—*Int.*

For I stole California from the Mexican land,
Fought in the bloody Civil War,
Yes, I even killed my brothers,

And so many others,
But I ain't marchin' any more.

For I marched to the battles of the German
  trench
In a war that was bound to end all wars;
I must have killed a million men,
And now they want me back again,
But I ain't marchin' any more.—*Int.*

For I flew the final mission in the Japanese
  skies,
Set off the mighty mushroom roar,
When I saw the cities burnin',
I knew that I was learnin'
That I ain't marchin' any more.

Now the labor leader's screamin' when they
  close the missile plants,
United Fruit screams at the Cuban shore,
Call it "Peace" or call it "Treason,"
Call it "Love" or call it "Reason,"
But I ain't marchin' any more.

AIN'T GWINE STUDY WAR NO MORE

Here another old spiritual comes out against regulations. The date and local origin of this one would be good to know; it antedates our recent wars of course.

Gwine to lay down my sword and shield, down by the riverside,
Down by the riverside, down by the riverside.
Gwine to lay down my sword and shield, down by the riverside,
Ain't gwine study war no more.

I ain't gwine study war no more, ain't gwine study war no more,
Ain't gwine study war no more. *(Repeat.)*

Gwine to stick my sword in the golden sand, down by the riverside,
Down by the riverside, down by the riverside.
Gwine to stick my sword in the golden sand, down by the riverside,
Ain't gwine study war no more.

HELL, NO! I AIN'T GONNA GO!

A SNCC song with words and music by Matthew Jones and Elaine Laron, this one is recorded by and available from SNCC. Published both in Broadside *and in* Sing Out! *as transcribed by Sis Cunningham. Copyright 1968 by Matthew Jones and Elaine Laron. Used by permission.*

Refrain:
Up tight! That's right!
I ain't gonna go! Hell, no!

I ain't goin' to Vietnam—
I ain't dyin' for Uncle Sam—*Ref.*

I ain't goin' to Vietnam—
I ain't burnin' my brothers to serve the man!
                                    —*Ref.*

I ain't goin' to Vietnam,
The Vietcong's just like I am.

Up tight! Up tight! Up tight!

Let's run it down, Brother Brown,
Tell every cat just where it's at.
I've had enough of Charlie's stuff.
If he messes with me I'm gonna get rough.
                                    —*Ref.*

IT AIN'T REALLY TRUE

Written by Peter Crabtree to the tune of "My Darling Nellie Gray," this one appeared in Broadside. *Copyright 1963 by Peter Crabtree.*

Well, I met a man this morning,
He was looking mighty blue,
And he said "We're bound to have a war,
We are heading for disaster,
And there's nothing we can do,
And there's no use in trying anymore."

Chorus:
Well, it ain't really true
'Cause it's up to me and you;
It's the pathway of peace
We've got to find.
If we all keep on tryin',
We can save the world from dyin'
'Cause it ain't that hard to save mankind.

Well, I met another buddy,
He was looking mighty mad,
And he said, "It looks like war's the only way,
'Cause the world situation
Is so bad in every nation
Might as well get it over with today."—*Cho.*

I can't help but have the notion
That the folks across the ocean
Don't want to fight a war no more than me;
If they all go out to fight it
I don't want to be invited,
'Cause the point of it is more than I can see.
—*Cho.*

WINDHAM

Some two hundred years ago, Isaac Watts wrote the lyrics for this one, with music, also from the eighteenth century, by Daniel Reed.

Broad is the road that leads to death,
And thousands walk together there.
But wisdom shows a narrow path
With here and there a traveller.

I DECLARE THE WAR IS OVER

Standing on the steps of the Pentagon, on October 21, 1967, the author of this lyric sang his own song. Words and music by Phil Ochs. Copyright 1968 by Barricade Music, Inc. All rights reserved. Used by permission.

Silent soldiers on a silver screen
Framed in fantasies and drugged in dreams,
Unpaid actors of the mystery,
The mad director knows that freedom will
    not make you free.
And what's this got to do with me?

Chorus:
I declare the war is over!
It's over!
It's over!

So do your duty boys and join with pride;
Serve your country in her suicide;
Prove your courage in the proud parade;
Trust your leaders where mistakes are almost
    never made,
And they're afraid that I'm afraid,
Yes, I'm afraid the war is over.—*Cho.*

Cardboard cowboys of a new frontier,
Drowning Indians in vats of beer;
The troops are leaving on the trojan train;
The sun is in their eyes but I am hiding from
    the rain.

Now one of us must be insane.—*Cho.*

But at least we're working building tanks and
    planes,
And a raise is coming so we can't complain.
The strong will wonder if they're surely
    strong;
It doesn't matter lately whether we are right
    or wrong,
But surely we've gone on too long.—*Cho.*

One-legged veterans will greet the dawn,
And they're whistling marches as they mow
    the lawn;
And the gargoyles only sit and grieve;
The gypsy fortuneteller told me that we've
    been deceived,
You only are what you believe.'

And I believe the war is over,
It's over!
It's over!

XI

SONGS AGAINST PREJUDICE

It is perhaps a testimony to the basic decency of the human race, or a self-protective quality of good music, that few songs known to the modern world are hymns of hate against people. Those most celebrated, the original "Hymn of Hate," the "Horst Wessel Song," and "Giovanezza," are now hard to find, even in American libraries. If "You Have to Be Taught" prejudice, as the hit song from *South Pacific* insists, few countries are consciously teaching it in the atomic age.

Our own era has instead developed a number of protest songs against prejudice, while the long circulation of popular songs expressing sympathy for peoples in voluntary or involuntary exile has helped understanding around the world.

I DON'T WANT TO PLAY IN YOUR YARD

Back in 1894, when this song was written by Philip Wingate and H. W. Petrie, it was just mildly funny. In the present state of racial and other tensions, it is possible to read into it a serious meaning.

I don't want to play in your yard,
I don't like you any more.
You'll be sorry when you see me
Sliding down our cellar door.

You can't holler down our rain barrel,
You can't climb our apple tree.
I don't want to play in your yard
If you won't be good to me.

NO IRISH NEED APPLY

Although the wave of Irish immigration was voluntary, as escape from poverty and unfair discrimination, there were trying conditions in this country as well. The lyric is by J. F. Poole, the musical arrangement by Pete Seeger.

I'm a decent boy just landed from the town of Ballyfad,
I want a situation, and I want it very bad.
I have seen employment advertised—" 'Tis just the thing," says I.
But the dirty spalpeen ended with "No Irish need apply."

Refrain:
Some do count it a misfortune to be christened Pat or Dan,
But to me it is an honor to be born an Irishman.

"Whoa," says I, "but that's an insult, though to get the place I'll try."
So I went to see this blackguard with his "No Irish need apply."—*Ref.*

STRANGERS IN YOUR TOWN

That the first Americans should be treated as "foreigners" seems strange indeed, but if anyone spoke fairly for them it was Peter La Farge, who wrote this song to the old tune "Kevin Barry." Copyright 1963 by Peter La Farge. Used by permission.

Chorus:
I'm an Indian, I'm an alien,
I'm a stranger in your town.
All your pretty roads lead upward,
All my pathways lead me down.

And the dark fields flow around me,
And the shadows deep as snow,
But the road says keep on singin'
And the road knows where I go.
For there's got to be somebody,
Indian or not,
To be singin' on the dark road
To open up the lock. And—

Chorus:
I'm an Indian, I'm an alien,
I'm a stranger in your town.

All your white man's roads lead upward,
All my red man's lead me down.

You can fill up all your prisons,
Lock and bar the door,
But for everyone you lock up
There'll be a thousand more;
For the red man and the black man,
The yellow and the brown,
We walk this road together
And this road is freedom bound.

Chorus:
Then the Indians won't be aliens,
Won't be strangers in your town,
And we all will walk together
On the road that's freedom bound.

JIM CROW

Introduced by Thomas Dartmouth Rice at the old Bowery Theatre in 1832, this song itself has been a victim of prejudice. Innocuous in intent, as just a dialect song in the days of Irish, Jewish, and German dialect humor, it was described as "the first blackface song to characterize a Negro sympathetically," and was perhaps the first American song to make a hit abroad. It was also credited with introducing Negro dancing to the stage. But popularity made the title synonymous with "Negro," and like that word as corrupted by mispronunciation, the name became an insult. The Jim of the song is a stock comedy type, telling in twenty-one verses of his skill with the ladies, with the fiddle, and in a presidential meeting. He also plugs the advantages of Virginia over Washington.

Come listen all you gals and boys, I'm just from Tuckyhoe;
I'm goin' to sing a leetle song, my name's Jim Crow.
Wheel about, and turn about, and do jis so—
Eb'ry time I wheel about, I jump Jim Crow.

I'm a roarer on the fiddle, and down in Ole Virginny
De say I play it scientific like Massa Paganini.

I went down to de river, I didn't mean to stay,
But there the gals they charm me so I couldn't get away.

An' when I cast the sheep's eye, then they all fall in lub;
I took my choice among 'em there and pick Miss Dinah Scrub.

The other gals begin to fight, I told 'em wait a bit,
I'd take 'em all, just one by one, as I thought fit.

I whip the lion of the West, I eat the alligator;
I put more water in my mouth than boil ten load o' tater.

The darkies in New Orleans, they think themselves so fine,
But darkies in Virginny, they all be so black they shine.

I sets upon the bull's horn, I hops upon this toe,
I tie the sarpent round my neck and then I dance just so.

In Washington the President he ax me what I do,
And give me so much money the others want it too.

And then I go to New York to put 'em right all there,
But find so many thick heads I give up in despair.

WE ARE AMERICANS TOO

In the war that was to break down so many racial barriers, this song, by Andy Razaf, Eubie Blake, and Charles Cooke, combining patriotism and protest, put the case for integration in the army and progress in civilian life. Copyright 1941 by W. C. Handy Music Company. All rights reserved. Used by permission.

Shouting loud Hosannas! Waving spangled
  banners
Seems to be the order of the day.
We are not exotic, or less patriotic,
Now you have the reason why we say:

Chorus:
By the record we've made, and the part that
  we've played,
WE ARE AMERICANS TOO.
By the pick and the plow and the sweat of our
  brow,
WE ARE AMERICANS TOO.

We have given up our blood and bone,
Helped to lay the Nation's cornerstone;
None have loved Old Glory more than we,
Or have shown a greater loyalty.
Bunker Hill to the Rhine,
We've been right there in line,
Serving the Red, White and Blue.
All our future is here, everything we hold
  dear—
WE ARE AMERICANS TOO!

STRANGE FRUIT

This is a really shocking song about racial injustice, and while it cannot be credited with the end of lynching, being unknown to persons likely to commit that crime, it did impress others who heard it and went on to write other protest songs. Words and music by Lewis Allan. Copyright 1948 by Edward Marks Music Corporation. All rights reserved. Used by permission.

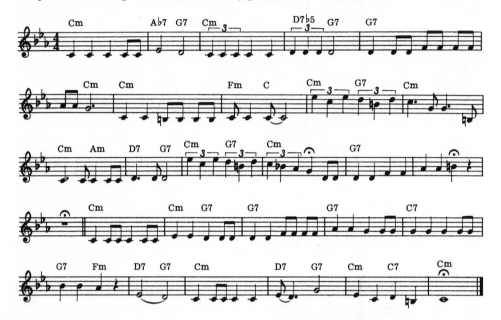

Southern trees bear a strange fruit,
Blood on the leaves and blood at the root,
Black body swinging in the southern breeze,
Strange fruit hanging from the poplar trees.
Pastoral scene of the gallant south,
The bulging eyes and the twisted mouth,

Scent of magnolia sweet and fresh,
And the sudden smell of burning flesh!
Here is a fruit for the crows to pluck,
For the rain to gather, for the wind to suck,
For the sun to rot, for a tree to drop,
Here is a strange and bitter crop.

BLACK, BROWN, AND WHITE BLUES

All the blues songs, beginning with the Handy classics, were effective protests, even though indirect. This one is specific in its recital of unfairness. Words and music by William Broonzy. Copyright 1946 by William Broonzy. Used by permission.

Just listen to this song I'm singin', brother—
You'll know it's true.
If you're black and got to work for a living, boy,
This is what they'll say:

Chorus:
Now, if you're white, you're right,
And if you're brown, stick around;
But if you're black—
Oh, brother, git back, git back, git back.

I was in an employment office;
I got a number and got in line.
They called everybody's number,
But they never did call mine.—*Cho.*

Me and a man working side by side;
This is what it meant:
He was getting a dollar an hour,
When I was making fifty cents.—*Cho.*

I helped to build this country;
I fought for it, too.
Now . . . I want to know
What you gonna do about Jim Crow?—*Cho.*

Chorus:
Now, if you're white, you're right,
And if you're brown, stick around;
But if you're black—
Oh, brother, git back, git back, git back.

DO RUSSIAN PEOPLE STAND FOR WAR?

Here is a song to counteract blind anti-Russian sentiment. Saying Niet *in advance of a world conflict feared by many, this counterpropaganda song with words by Y. Yevtushenko and music by E. Kolmanovsky was translated for Broadside magazine by Olga Moisseyenko, Tom Williams, and Sis Cunningham.*

Do Russian people stand for war?
Go ask the sons on plain and shore;
Those sons and daughters answer best
Whose soldier-fathers lie at rest
Beneath the birch and poplar tree;
The answer given silently
Will none the less be strong and sure—
Ask them if Russians are,
Ask them if Russians are,
Ask them if Russians are for war.

Those soldiers died on every hand
Not only for their own dear land
But so the world at night could sleep
And never have to wake and weep;
Go ask the soldiers from the ranks
The lads you hugged on Elbe's banks
And who remember all they saw—
Ask them if Russians are,

Ask them if Russians are,
Ask them if Russians are for war.

Sure we know how to fight a war,
But we don't want to see once more
The soldiers falling all around,
Their countryside a battleground;
Ask those who gave the soldiers life,
Go ask the mother, ask the wife,
And you will have to ask no more
If Russian people are,
If Russian people are,
If Russian people are for war. . . .

The working people of each land
Will come for sure to understand,
Throughout the world on sea and shore;
Ask them if Russians are,
Ask them if Russians are,
Ask them if Russians are for war.

MY DOG'S BIGGER THAN YOUR DOG

As another song said, you have to be taught; but young children learn early to compete with the folks next door, and their elders, so educated, are willing to unloose the dogs of war. Written by Tom Paxton. Copyright 1963 by Cherry Lane Music. All rights reserved. Used by permission.

My dog's bigger than your dog,
My dog's bigger than yours.
My dog's bigger an' he chases mailmen,
My dog's bigger than yours.

Chorus:
I'm not afraid of the dark any more, I can tie
    my shoe.
I've been to the country, and I am goin' to
    school.

Our car's faster than your car,
Our car's faster than yours.
It has a louder horn; it bumps other cars;
Our car's faster than yours.—*Cho.*

My dad's meaner than your dad,
My dad's meaner than yours;
My dad's meaner and he yells louder,
My dad's meaner than yours.—*Cho.*

XII

SONGS OF SOCIAL SIGNIFICANCE

That our era is one of far-reaching social change is now generally understood. Within comparatively recent memory, American women and southern Negroes have gained political rights and obtained important economic concessions. Many persons are becoming aware of atomic-age potentials not only in terms of war danger but also in terms of the elimination of poverty as an alternate to war abroad and unrest at home. Some of our established beliefs concerning religion and education are being earnestly questioned.

That successful protests against the untenable, and even practical, proposals for change may be made in terms of music and that no country measuring social progress in such terms can show a more vital musical history than the United States are due largely to the contributions of American Negroes. In their suffrage campaign women, too, marched in the streets; but their relatively quick and easy success in this country was owed in part to the example of militant Englishwomen who, before them, went to jail, were trampled by policemen's horses, threw rocks at government buildings, and set fire to mailboxes. Negro rights were won more slowly, over the decades and the centuries, and their songs from slavery days—"Go Down, Moses," the surprise victory of "Jericho" and the promise of progress in "De Old Ark A-Moverin'"—are only now understood to have social as well as religious

meaning. The most effective songs of the early labor movement and those of today for civil rights and peace are based on hymn tunes and spirituals.

Of course, not all the good tunes were religious. The "blues" also had their message, and if you hated to see that evening sun go down, you had good reason. In time more outspoken songs—"Back of the Bus," for instance —made the meaning clear. The outstanding success in the civil-rights field, indirectly quoted by Mrs. Martin Luther King at the memorial service for her husband in Memphis, has of course been "Blowin' in the Wind." Such, indeed, has been the song's popularity that it may not matter that Bob Dylan's publishers now deny permission to quote. You know it anyhow.

With the success of young songwriters from the universities, almost every problem of today has been subject to musical attack. Current songs ask to save the dunes or the coyotes, as well as to save the world from war. An old song begged the woodman to spare that tree; what about the redwoods? What about new Memphis blues or Dallas blues in memory of assassinations? Write your own ticket for a new world in more songs. You and your friends can sing them, perhaps get them printed in *Broadside*, perhaps go on the air—although even Pete Seeger (see "Waist Deep in the Big Muddy") had his troubles there.

SING ME A SONG WITH SOCIAL SIGNIFICANCE

The famous union musical Pins and Needles, *with songs by Harold Rome, provided the hit song that led the parade of protest songs. Copyright 1937 by Mills Music, Inc. All rights reserved. Used by permission.*

Sing me a song with social significance,
All other tunes are taboo.
I want a ditty with heat in it,
Appealing with feeling and meat in it!
Sing me a song with social significance
Or you can sing till you're blue—
Let meaning shine from ev'ry line,
Or I won't love you.

Sing me of wars and sing me of breadlines,
Tell me of front-page news.
Sing me of strikes and last-minute headlines,
Dress your observation in syncopation,
Sing me a song with social significance,
There's nothing else that will do—
It must get hot with what is what
Or I won't love you.

Sing me a song with social significance,
All other tunes are taboo.
I want a song that's satirical,
And putting the mere into miracle.
Sing me a song with social significance
Or you can sing till you're blue—
It must be packed with social fact
Or I won't love you.

Sing me of kings and con'frences martial,
Tell me of mills and mines.
Sing me of courts that aren't impartial,
What's to be done with 'em, tell me in rhyme!
Sing me a song with social significance,
There's nothing else that will do—
It must be tense with common sense,
Or I won't love you.

MARCH OF THE PEERS

Back in the eighties W. S. Gilbert was a social as well as political observer, and Iolanthe, *with its chorus of peers of the realm, poked fun at the whole British social structure. Although the United States has no peerage, it can hardly claim a classless society, and the opera's message is clear. Sullivan's music helps.*

Bow, bow, ye lower middle classes!
Bow, bow, ye tradesmen, bow, ye masses;
Blow the trumpets, bang the brasses,
Tan-tan-ta-ra! Tzing! boom!
Bow, bow, ye lower middle classes!
Bow, bow, ye tradesmen, bow, ye masses;
Blow the trumpets, bang the brasses,

Tan-tan-ta-ra! Tzing boom, Tzing boom,
Tan-tan-ta-ra! Tzing boom!
Tan-tan-ta-ra! Tzing boom! Tzing boom!
Blow, blow the trumpets, bang the brasses!
Blow, blow the trumpets, bang the brasses!
Blow, blow the trumpets,
Blow, blow the trumpets!

WE NEVER SPEAK AS WE PASS BY

*Celebrated in its day, and laughed at later, this song reflected an actual social con-
dition: not merely the wronged husband, as here, but also the general public
"cut" a female transgressor. Frank Egerton wrote this in 1882.*

The spell is past, the dream is o'er,
And though we meet, we love no more.
One heart is crush'd to droop and die,
And for relief must heav'nward fly.

No life on earth more pure than ours
In that dear home midst field and flow'rs;

Until the tempter came to Nell—
It dazzled her, alas she fell.

We never speak as we pass by,
Although a tear bedims her eye;
I know she thinks of her past life
When we were loving man and wife.

IT'S THE SYME THE WHOLE WORLD OVER

This song, understood wherever English is spoken despite the cockney dialect, classifies people and privilege (first- or second-class citizens) in terms of opportunity, with prejudice against a lower class illustrated in terms of the unlucky girl. Australian soldiers sang the old song in England during the world wars.

It's the syme the whole world over,
It's the poor what gets the blyme,
While the rich 'as all the plysures.
Now ayn't that a blinkin' shyme?

She was a parson's daughter,
Pure, unstyn-ed was her fyme,
Till a country squire come courtin',
And the poor girl lorst 'er nyme.

So she went aw'y to Lunnon,
Just to 'ide her guilty shyme.
There she met an Army Chaplain:
Ornst ag'yn she lorst 'er nyme.

'Ear 'im as he jaws the Tommies,
Warnin' o' the flymes o' 'ell.
With 'er 'ole 'eart she had trusted,
But ag'yn she lorst 'er nyme.

Now 'e's in his ridin' britches,
'Untin' foxes in the chyse
W'ile the wictim o' his folly
Makes her livin' by her wice.

So she settled down in Lunnon,
Sinkin' deeper in her shyme,
Till she met a lybor leader,
And ag'yn she lorst 'er nyme.

Now 'e's in the 'Ouse o' Commons,
Mykin' laws to put down crime,
W'ile the wictim of his plysure
Walks the street each night in shyme.

Then there cyme a bloated bishop.
Marriage was the tyle 'e tole.
There was no one else to tyke 'er,
So she sold 'er soul for gold.

See 'er in 'er 'orse and carriage,
Drivin' d'ily through the park.
Though she's myde a wealthy marriage
Still she 'ides a brykin' 'eart.

In a cottage down in Sussex
Live's 'er payrents old and lyme,
And they drink the wine she sends them,
But they never, never, speaks 'er nyme.

In their poor and 'umble dwellin'
There 'er grievin' payrents live,
Drinkin' champyne as she sends 'em
But they never, never, can forgive.

It's the syme the whole world over,
It's the poor what gets the blyme,
While the rich 'as all the plysures.
Now, ayn't it a bloody shyme?

THE BLUE ALSATIAN MOUNTAINS

In Victorian parlors the status of women was illustrated by this once-popular tearjerker, in which, though the simple maiden is blameless, she is misled and "ruined."

By the blue Alsatian mountains dwelt a maiden young and fair,
Like the careless flowing fountains were the ripples of her hair, were the ripples
    of her hair;
Angel mild her eyes so winning, angel bright her happy smile,
When beneath the fountains spinning you could hear her song the while.

Adé, Adé, Adé, such songs will pass away,
Though the blue Alsatian mountains seem to watch and wait alway.

By the blue Alsatian mountains came a stranger in the spring,
And he lingered by the fountains just to hear the maiden sing, just to hear the
    maiden sing;
Just to whisper in the moonlight, words the sweetest she had known,
Just to charm away the hours till her heart was all his own.—*Cho.*

By the blue Alsatian mountains many springtimes bloomed and passed,
And the maiden by the fountains saw she'd lost her hopes at last, she lost her
    hopes at last.
And she withered like a flower that is waiting for the rain,
She will never see the stranger where the fountains fall again.—*Cho.*

JUST TELL THEM THAT YOU SAW ME

*For the truly "abandoned" woman, communication even with her family was im-
possible; she could not share the shame. Theodore Dreiser's brother, Paul Dresser,
composed this hit of the nineties.*

"Just tell them that you saw me,"
She said, "They'll know the rest.
Just tell them I was looking well, you know.
Just whisper, if you get the chance, to Mother
    dear, and say,

I love her as I did long, long ago, long, long
    ago."

LA DONNA É MOBILE
(Woman Is Fickle)

This famous aria from Verdi's opera Rigoletto *long afforded a handy explanation for what were considered unreasonable demands for the suffrage, and a reason for not granting it to women.*

Woman is fickle, false altogether;
Moves like a feather
Borne on the breezes.
Woman with witching smile will e'er
    deceive you,
Often will grieve you,
Yet as she pleases.
Her heart's unfeeling, false altogether,
Moves like a feather
Borne on the breeze.

Wretched the day is when she looks kindly,
Trusts to her blindly,
Her life thus wasting;
Yet he must surely be dull beyond measure
Who of love's happiness
Ne'er has been tasting.
Woman's unfeeling, false altogether,
Moves like a feather
Borne on the breeze.

SHE IS MORE TO BE PITIED . . .

"Than censured"—eventually moralists came to consider that the environment of an erring female, and her economic opportunities, might influence her conduct as much as original sin. Another gem of the nineties by William B. Gray.

At the old concert hall on the Bow'ry,
'Round a table were seated one night,
A crowd of young fellows carousing,
With them life seemed cheerful and bright.
At the very next table, was seated
A girl who had fallen to shame;
All the young fellows jeered at her weakness,
Till they heard an old woman explain:

Chorus:
She is more to be pitied than censured,
She is more to be helped than despised,
She is only a lassie who ventured,
On life's stormy path, ill-advised.

Do not scorn her with words fierce and bitter,
Do not laugh at her shame and downfall,
For a moment just stop and consider,
That a man was the cause of it all.

There's an old-fashioned church 'round the
    corner,
Where the neighbors all gathered one day,
While the parson was preaching a sermon,
O'er a soul that had just passed away.
'Twas this same wayward girl from the Bow'ry,
Who a life of adventure had led,
Did the clergyman jeer at her downfall?
No, he asked for God's Mercy and said—*Cho.*

DON SIMÓN DE MI VIDA

Spanish-speaking countries retain longest the Latin status of women, but even there times are changing. Here we have the surprise of elders everywhere. Copyright 1953 by People's Artists. Used by permission of present copyright holder, Sing Out!

Don Simón, Don Simón, looking backward
Over all of the years I have known,
Never once have I seen what we now see—
Ah, me, what a world, Don Simón!

In my day girls looked modestly downward,
In prayer as they walked to the church
Holding rosary beads in their fingers—
What a world we have now, Don Simón!

Don Simón, Don Simón, de mi vida
En los años que me dió el Señor,
Nunca he visto loque ahora he mirado,
Ha, que tiempo, Don Simón.

En mis tiempos las niñas asaban
Sus rosarios en la procesión,
Y sus ojos mostraban humildes,
Ha, que tiempo, Señor Don Simón.

THE POOR WORKING GIRL

This classic, of unknown origin, deals in four lines with four subjects—work, wages, crime, and girls.

The poor working girl, may heaven
     protect her,
She has such an aw'fly hard time.
The rich man's daughter goes haughtily by—
My God, do you wonder at crime?

NOW I AM MARRIED

Three folk songs—"Now I Am Married," and two opposing versions of "I Wish I Was Single Again," with many variants and undetermined authorship—have long been sung with feeling by those sharing one of the views expressed.

Now I am married, Sir John I'll not curse,
He joins us together for better or worse.

But if I were single, I'll tell you plain,
I would be advised ere I married again.

I WISH I WAS SINGLE AGAIN

I

I wish I was single again,
I wish I was single again,

For when I was single my pockets did jingle,
I wish I was single again.

I married a wife, oh, then, *(Repeat.)*
I married a wife, she's the curse of my life,
I wish I was single again.

My wife she died, oh, then, *(Repeat.)*
My wife she died, and I laughed till I cried
To think I was single again.

I married another, the devil's grandmother,
I wish I was single again.

Now listen all you young men, *(Repeat.)*
Be good to the first, for the next will be worse,
I wish I was single again.

I I

When I was single, marrying was my crave;
Now I am married and I'm troubled to my grave.
Now it's, oh, Lord, I wish I was a single girl again.

When I was single, I lived at my ease;
Now I am married with a husband to please.

When I was single, I was dressed so fine;
Now I am married, I go ragged all the time.

When I was single, my shoes they were new;
Now I am married and the water runs right through.

When I was single, I ate biscuits and pie;
Now I am married, it's eat cornbread or die.

Dishes to wash and the spring to go to,
No one to help me, I have it all to do.

A house full of children, and trouble they be,
None of them big enough to do the work for me.

If you are single, hear what I say—
Don't crave to be married or you'll rue the day.

MAN SMART—WOMAN SMARTER

The calypso version states a heresy seldom expressed, but one that men sometimes find it smart to suggest. Calypso songs of all periods (this is an old one) frequently provide views refreshingly different from those currently accepted.

Let us put man and woman together
To find out which one is smarter.
Some say man, but I say no.
Woman got the man beat, I should know.

Chorus: Not me! But the people they say,
The men are leading the woman astray.
But I say that the woman of today
Smarter than the man in ev'ry way.

MY DARLING NELLIE GRAY

Although Negro women, faced with two handicaps, were among the first to gain a relative independence, they were indeed helpless in the pre-Civil War period, and this old song brought tears even in the South.

There's a low green valley on the old Kentucky shore
Where I've whiled many happy hours away,
A-sitting and a-singing by the little cottage door
Where lived my darling Nellie Gray.

Chorus:
Oh, my poor Nellie Gray,
They have taken her away
And I'll never see my darling any more.
They have taken her to Georgia,
There to wear her life away
Far, far from the old Kentucky shore.

When the moon had climbed the mountain, and the stars were shining too,
Then I'd take my darling Nellie Gray,
And we'd float down the river in my little red canoe,
While my banjo sweetly I would play.

Chorus:
Oh, my darling Nellie Gray
Up in heaven, there they say
That they'll never take you from me any more.
I'm a-coming, coming, coming,
As the angels clear the way—
Farewell to the old Kentucky shore.

TURN AROUND, MISS LIBERTY

Lady Liberty herself is here invited by Len Chandler to consider the state of the "deep South," where the rights of men, women, and children are not always recognized, even now. Copyright 1963 by Fall River Music Co. All rights reserved. Used by permission.

Every eye in the whole wide world is lookin' toward the U.S.A.
Miss Liberty stands with her torch held high, but she's lookin' the other way.

Chorus:
Turn around, turn around, Miss Liberty,

Turn around I say.
Touch your torch to the cotton curtain,
Shed a little light our way.

Old folks there are not forgotten, look away, look away.
Cotton balls ain't the only thing rotten down Mississippi way.—*Cho.*

Shine gently in that lonely room where a widowed mother weeps;
Shine fiercely in that killer's eyes that he may know no sleep.—*Cho.*

We're here, we're tired, we're poor, we're huddled masses yearning to be free,
And Liberty stands with her head held high and her torch still out to sea.—*Cho.*

Forty million eyes by now like silent fuses glow,
I hear their gentle voices calling No Jim Crow.
                    [Traditional melody "Old Black Joe"]—*Cho.*

Shine in the corners of the hearts that hate and can't forgive;
Reveal the reason that we die and how we want to live.—*Cho.*

NOW, RIGHT NOW!

*Woman, the practical sex, keeps nagging; in this song a Negro mother demands
to know why these things must be, and for how long. Copyright 1952 by Sing Out,
Inc. Used by permission.*

I met a Negro mother, her head was bent and low.
She said, "Why do the po-lice treat my people so?"
They beat us and they starve us, while justice passes by.
That's why I'll fight for freedom and hold my head up high."

Chorus:
Now, right now; now, right now; now's the time for freedom,
Now, right now. Do right now. Fight right now.
Fight the fight for freedom, now, right now.

I met a Negro soldier, coming from the war.
I asked that Negro soldier what he'd been fighting for.
Said that Negro soldier, "Me, I took a vow,
I was fighting for my freedom and I want it now, right now."—*Cho.*

I've had my share of troubles. I've had my share and more,
But I added up my troubles, and now I know the score.
Our wrongs shall all be righted, our strength shall show us how,
With Negroes and whites united, I mean now, right now.—*Cho.*

IT MUST HAVE BEEN ANOTHER COUNTRY

Phil Ochs refuses to believe that some of the things protest songs are written about could really happen here. Copyright 1963 by Appleseed Music. All rights reserved. Used by permission.

Oh, a rifle took its aim and a man fell to the ground.
He tried to stand again but everybody held him down.
A time of terror when a bullet pierced the air—
I know that couldn't happen here.

Chorus:
So it must have been another country,
Yes, it must have been another land.
That couldn't happen in the U.S.A.—
We'd never treat a man that way.

And a man is workin' steady, it's good money he receives,
But he's thrown out of work for the wrong things he believes;
He didn't have the thoughts most everybody shares,
I know that couldn't happen here.—*Cho.*

And a migrant worker sweats underneath the burnin' sun,
He's fallen on his knees but his work is never done;
He begs someone to listen but nobody seems to care,
And I know that couldn't happen here.—*Cho.*

And a man is sent to prison to wait until he dies,
He fights to save his life, for years and years he tries;
Even though he changed himself he dies upon the chair,
I know that couldn't happen here.—*Cho.*

THE BALLAD OF MARTIN LUTHER KING

Many songs will be written about the great leader, but this one by Poor Boy Michael Strange, published in Broadside, *appeared first. Copyright 1968 by Poor Boy Michael Strange. Used by permission.*

Gather round me, friends, I have a song to sing
About a hero of our time named Martin Luther King.
Martin Luther King was born to a sharecropper's son,
And every racist feared him, and he never owned a gun.

Chorus:
And I've been to the mountaintop,
And today I have a dream—
Don't you ever forget the words of Martin Luther King.

Now, a bus line in Montgomery had some folks sit in back,
And it wasn't a coincidence that all these folks were black;
Then Martin Luther King called a boycott in that town
He just walked with his people and they shut that busline down.—*Cho.*

Now he preached and lived non-violence until the very end
On a hotel porch in Memphis, Mankind lost its best friend;
'Cause he fought for human rights as he rode from town to town,
And that's what he was doing in Memphis when some redneck shot him down.
—*Cho.*

Now it's time to take a look in that mirror on the wall.
Did you help pull the trigger or weren't you there at all?
And the sickness of a nation then soon becomes quite clear
When they kill a man with hatred because he wouldn't die from fear.—*Cho.*

And I've been to the mountaintop,
And today I had a dream—
My friends, those are the very words of Martin Luther King.

BIRMINGHAM JAIL

*Also known as "Down in the Valley," this old folk song sung by Leadbelly took
on new life for its mention of a jail now famous for the distinction of some of its
inmates, who included Martin Luther King.*

Down in the valley,
The valley so low,
Hang your head over,
Hear the wind blow.

Hear the wind blow, love,
Hear the wind blow.
Hang your head over,
Hear the wind blow.

Roses love sunshine,
Violets love dew,

Angels in heaven
Know I love you.

Write me a letter,
Send it by mail,
Send it in care of
The Birmingham Jail.

Birmingham Jail,
Birmingham Jail,
Send it in care of
The Birmingham Jail.

FREEDOM RIDER

One of the earlier desegregation songs explains how further changes began on the bus lines down South. Lyrics by Marilyn Eisenberg. Copyright 1961 by Marilyn Eisenberg; first published in Broadside. *The tune is that of "Hully Gully."*

Went to Mississippi on a Greyhound bus line—
Freedom, Freedom Rider.
Went into the terminal and everything was fine—
Freedom, Freedom Rider.
Sitting in a waiting room, trying to buy a ticket,
Maybe get some coffee too.

Police said to me, "Move out and move on,"
Freedom, Freedom Rider.
I just kept a-sitting there, not doin' nothing wrong—
Freedom, Freedom Rider.
I'm a Freedom Rider, he's a Freedom Rider
You can be a Freedom Rider too.

They took me up to jail in a big black paddy wagon—
Freedom, Freedom Rider.
I sang all the way, my spirit wasn't dragging—
Freedom, Freedom Rider.
We shall overcome and we shall not be moved,
And climbing Jacob's ladder too.

Well, I went before the judge and what did he say—
Freedom, Freedom Rider.
"You've breached the peace, now in jail you must stay,
Freedom, Freedom Rider.
Pay two hundred dollars because you are so guilty;
Stay in jail for four months too."

I didn't pay my fine, although I want to be free—
Freedom, Freedom Rider.
They carried me off to the penitentiary—
Freedom, Freedom Rider
"I'll throw you in the hole, I'll take away your mattress,
You damn Yankee agitator, you!"

Now behind the bars I keep singing this song—
Freedom, Freedom Rider.
Freedom's comin' and it won't be long—
Freedom, Freedom Rider.
I'm a Freedom Rider, he's a Freedom Rider,
You can be a Freedom Rider too.

POLICEMAN'S LOT

Even policemen can be sympathetic. Here W. S. Gilbert, in a famous song from
The Pirates of Penzance, explains—with music by Sir Arthur Sullivan—how a
sensitive cop can suffer.

When a felon's not engaged in his employment, his employment,
Or maturing his felonious little plans, little plans,
His capacity for innocent enjoyment, 'cent enjoyment,
Is just as great as any honest man's, honest man's.
Our feelings we with difficulty smother, 'culty smother,
When constabulary duty's to be done, to be done.
Ah, take one consideration with another, with another,
A policeman's lot is not a happy one.
Ah! When constabulary duty's to be done, to be done,
A policeman's lot is not a happy one, happy one.

When the enterprising burglar's not a-burgling, not a-burgling,
When the cutthroat isn't occupied in crime, 'pied in crime,
He loves to hear the little brook a-gurgling, brook a-gurgling,
And listen to the merry village chime, village chime.
When the coster's finished jumping on his mother, on his mother,
He loves to lie a-basking in the sun, in the sun.
Ah! Take one consideration with another, with another,
A policeman's lot is not a happy one, happy one.

Verse for 1969:
When a copper has to shoot a flower maiden, flower maiden,
When he has to hit a hippie on the head, on the head,
Though with praises from the mayor he's o'erladen, he's o'erladen,
Still he finds it hard to earn his daily bread, daily bread.
When he's asked to tell one riot from another, from another,
A policeman's lot is not a happy one, happy one.

BROTHER, THAT AIN'T GOOD!

The case against poverty in a rich country is put by Matthew Jones and Elaine Laron. Copyright 1968 by Matthew Jones and Elaine Laron; first published in Broadside. Used by permission.

When one man's got millions and
Another ain't got a dime,
That's when law and order's just
Another name for crime.
Here's one simple fact of life
That must be understood:
The rich are rich because the poor are poor,
And, brother, that ain't good.

Chorus:
That ain't good, that ain't good, that ain't
    good,
That ain't good for me and my brothers,
And, brother, that ain't good.

You've got the right to starve me and
I've got the right to cry;
You've got the right to kill me and
I've got the right to die.
You say I must respect your rights,
I don't see how I could.
If rights for you mean wrongs for me,
Well, brother, that ain't good.—*Cho.*

You tell me you're my brother as
We join our hands and sing,
You tell me how you've always loved
Martin Luther King.
But you are also brother to
The man who wears the hood,
You've got too many brothers, man,
And, brother, that ain't good.—*Cho.*

All you two-faced politicians who
Sing we shall overcome
But support the institutions
I need liberation from,
Well *you* and *me* ain't *"we,"* my friend,
Let this be understood.
It's you who we shall overcome,
And, brother, that *is* good.

Final chorus:
That *is* good, that *is* good, that *is* good,
That is good for me and my brothers,
And, brother, that *is* good.

IT ISN'T NICE

Young reformers faced disapproval, but not always from their elders. Malvina Reynolds, who wrote this one, is a grandmother. Copyright 1964 by Schroder Music Company. All rights reserved. Used by permission.

It isn't nice to block the doorways,
Isn't nice to go to jail.
There are nicer ways to do it,
But the nice ways always fail.
It isn't nice, it isn't nice,
You told us once, you told us twice,
But if that is Freedom's price,
We don't mind.

It isn't nice to carry banners
Or to sleep in on the floor,
Or to shout or cry of Freedom
At the hotel and the store.
It isn't nice, it isn't nice,
You told us once, you told us twice,
But if that is Freedom's price,
We don't mind.

Well, we've tried negotiations
And the three-man picket line,
Mr. Charlie didn't see us
And he might as well be blind.
Now our new ways aren't nice,
When we deal with men of ice,
But if that is Freedom's price,
We don't mind.

How about those years of lynchings
And the shot in Evers' back?
Did you say it wasn't proper,
Did you stand upon the track?
You were quiet just like mice,
Now you say *we* aren't nice,
And if that is Freedom's price,
We don't mind.

WORRIED MAN BLUES

This one goes back to the days of chain gangs and early proposals to reform the penal system, even for those convicted of old-fashioned antisocial behavior.

It takes a worried man to sing a worried song, *(Repeat twice.)*
I'm worried now, but I won't be worried long.

I went across the river, and I lay down to sleep, *(Repeat twice.)*
When I awoke, there were shackles on my feet.

(Similarly:) Twenty-nine links of chain around my leg,
And on each link an initial of my name.

I asked the judge, now what might be my fine,
Twenty-one years on the R.C. Mountain Line.

Twenty-one years to pay my awful crime,
Twenty-one years, but I've still got ninety-nine.

The train arrived, sixteen coaches long,
The girl I love is on that train and gone.

I looked down the track as far as I could see,
Litty bitty hand was waving after me.

If anyone asks you who composed this song,
Tell him it was I, and I sing it all day long.

BURN, BABY, BURN

Jimmy Collier, the author and composer, says this song was written during the Watts riot. The "Learn, baby, learn" refrain is of course a quote from responsible leaders of the "Movement." Copyright 1966 by Jimmy Collier. First published in Broadside.

I called President Johnson on the phone,
The secretary said he wasn't there;
I tried to get in touch with Mr. Humphrey;
They couldn't find him anywhere.
I went into the courtroom, with my poor sad face;
Didn't have no money, didn't have no lawyer;
They wouldn't plead my case,

Chorus:
So I said a burn, baby, burn,
Nowhere to be, no me to see;
I said a Nowhere to turn, burn, baby, burn.

I really wanted a decent job, I really needed some scratch
(I heard people talking about a dream, now, a dream that I couldn't catch);
I really wanted to be somebody and all I had was a match;
Couldn't get oil from Rockefeller's wells,
Couldn't get diamonds from the mine,
If I can't enjoy the American dream, won't be water but fire next time.—*Cho.*

Walkin' around on the west side now, lookin' mean and mad;
Deep down inside my heart, I'm feeling sorry and sad;
Got a knife and a razor blade, everybody that I know is tough,
But when I tried to burn my way out of the ghetto,
I burned my own self up, when I said,—*Cho.*

Learn, baby learn, learn, baby, learn;
You need a concern, you've got money to earn,
You've got midnight oil to burn, baby, burn.

I really want a decent education,
I really want a decent place to stay,
I really want some decent clothes, now,
I really want a decent family,
I really want a decent life like everybody else. . . .

POOR BOY

Also known as "Coon Can," author unknown, this old-timer is here given in a Texas version—Huntsville Penitentiary is in that state. Ten years was a light sentence if the crime was murder.

My mother called me to her deathbed side, these words she said to me:
"If you don't mend your rovin' ways, they'll put you in the penitentiary,
They'll put you in the penitentiary, poor boy, they'll put you in the penitentiary,
If you don't mend your rovin' ways, they'll put you in the penitentiary."

I sat me down to play coon can, could scarcely read my hand,
A thinkin' about the woman I loved, ran away with another man.
Ran away with another man, poor boy, ran away with another man.
I was thinkin' about the woman I loved, ran away with another man.

I'm a standin' on the corner, in front of a jewelry store,
Big policeman taps me on the back, says, "You ain't a goin' to kill no more."
Says, "You ain't a goin' to kill no more, poor boy," says, "You ain't a goin'
    to kill no more."
Big policeman taps me on the back, says, "You ain't a goin' to kill no more."

"Oh, cruel, kind judge, oh, cruel, kind judge, what are you goin' to do with me?"
"If that jury finds you guilty, poor boy, I'm goin' to send you to the penitentiary.
I'm goin' to send you to the penitentiary, poor boy, goin' to send you to the
    penitentiary.
If that jury finds you guilty, poor boy, I'm goin' to send you to the penitentiary."

Well, the jury found him guilty, the clerk he wrote it down,
The judge pronounced his sentence, poor boy; ten long years in Huntsville town.
Ten long years in Huntsville town, poor boy, ten long years in Huntsville town;
The judge pronounced his sentence, poor boy, ten long years in Huntsville town.

The iron gate clanged behind him, he heard the warden say,
"Ten long years for you in prison, poor boy, yes, it's ten long years for you this
    day.
Ten long years for you in prison, poor boy, yes, it's ten long years this day."
As the iron gate clanged behind him, that's what he heard the warden say.

I'M GOIN' TO GET MY BABY OUTA JAIL

Today the difference between the kids jailed for crimes and those behind bars for trying to change the world is that the criminals "want out" and the world-changers are proud to be there. Len H. Chandler makes the point clear in this song. Copyright 1964 by Fall River Music. Used by permission.

Chorus:
I'm goin' to get my baby outa jail,
I'm goin' to get my baby outa jail.
She said she wasn't guilty, and she wouldn't pay no bail;
I'm goin' to get my baby outa jail.

My baby wouldn't let me pay her fine, *(Repeat.)*
She said she wasn't guilty and she wouldn't pay one dime;
But—*Cho.*

You know I must have walked a valley on my floor *(Repeat.)*
Just waitin' for her footsteps and her knockin' at my door;
But—*Cho.*

Well, they phoned and said the word had come today, *(Repeat.)*
Now I'm meetin' all the lawyers at the courthouse right away;
Yes,—*Cho.*

The highest courts all honored her appeal, *(Repeat.)*
They said she wasn't guilty and she got a dirty deal,
So—*Cho.*

Every po-lice in this country knows her name, *(Repeat.)*
But I'm goin' to get my baby just the same
Yes,—*Cho.*

Only one thing more keeps workin' on my mind, *(Repeat.)*
If high court costs and lawyers' fees ain't something like a fine,
But—*Cho.*

JESSE'S CORRIDO

This was written to commemorate a death sentence, later commuted to life imprisonment, under which the state of Utah would have executed a Mexican-American boy, aged sixteen, for murder. Newspaper disclosure of prison scandal brought the commutation. The words are by Bruce Phillips; the music is by Rosalie Sorrells. Copyright 1969 by Folk Legacy Records, Sharon, Conn. Published by Sing Out! All rights reserved. Used by permission.

On the corners together you'll find us,
By the lamp posts at night we'll be there,
Our spirits like smoke that blows
        through the night,
Restless and goin' nowhere.

Trouble is all we can give you,
Trouble is all we have known.
Our lives like water that runs
        through our hands,
Leavin' us unloved and alone.

Our fathers, they say, were just like us.
Our children will all be the same . . .

Hair like black leather and skin
        brown as wood,
Speaking a low Spanish name.

The things that I do are all very bad things.
I do them and then don't know why.
You hold up your sons with their blue
        or brown eyes
And tell me they're better than I.

But tonight, when you sit at your table,
With your wife and your children close by,
Recall this corrido my red blood has made—
And now, mis amigos, goodbye.

THE DRUNKARD'S DOOM

Although modern drugs may be considered more serious an influence than alcohol, the old songs warned of strong drink; and if they failed to establish Prohibition, they did influence public opinion in their day.

At early dawn I saw a man,
Stand by the beer saloon;
His eyes were sunk, his lips were parched,
Oh, that's the drunkard's doom.

His little boy stood by his side,
And trembled as he said:
"Dear Father, Mother lies sick at home,
And sister cries for bread."

He rose and staggered to the bar,
As he had done before,
And begged of the landlord, "Give, oh, give,
Just give me one glass more."

The landlord granted his request,
He drank from the poisoned bowl,
He drank while the wife and children starved,
He ruined his poor soul.

Three years had passed, I went that way,
A crowd stood by the door;
I asked the cause, and one replied,
"The drunkard is no more."

I saw the hearse drive slowly away,
No wife, no child was there,
They to a better land had flown,
Beyond this world of care.

FATHER, COME HOME

Famous in its day was the emotional appeal of this one, in a class with that recitation about the face on the barroom floor. Whether any alcoholics responded is unknown, but Prohibition was voted in. Words and music by Henry C. Work.

Father, dear Father, come home with me now!
The clock in the steeple strikes one;
You said you were coming right home from
    the shop,
As soon as your day's work was done.
Our fire has gone out—our house is all dark—
And Mother's been watching since tea,
With poor brother Benny so sick in her arms,
And no one to help her but me.
Come home! come home! come home!
Please, Father, dear Father, come home.

Chorus:
Hear the sweet voice of the child,
Which the night winds repeat as they roam!
Oh, who could resist this most pleading of
    prayers?
"Please, Father, dear Father, come home!"

Father, dear Father, come home with me now!
The clock in the steeple strikes two.
The night has grown colder, and Benny is
    worse,
But he has been calling for you.
Indeed he is worse—Ma says he will die,
Perhaps before morning shall dawn;
And this is the message she sent me to bring,
"Come quickly or he will be gone."
Come home! come home! come home!
Please, Father, dear Father, come home.

Chorus:
Hear the sweet voice of the child,
Which the night winds repeat as they roam
Oh, who could resist this most pleading of
    prayers?
"Please, Father, dear Father, come home!"

Father, dear Father, come home with me now
The clock in the steeple strikes three;
The house is so lonely, the hours are so long
For poor weeping Mother and me.
Yes, we are alone—poor Benny is dead
And gone with the angels of light.
And these were the very last words that he
    said,
"I want to kiss Papa good night!"
Come home! come home! come home!
Please, Father, dear Father, come home.

Chorus:
Hear the sweet voice of the child,
Which the night winds repeat as they roam
Oh, who could resist this most pleading of
    prayers?
"Please, Father, dear Father, come home!"

THE UNSOCIABLE PIG

Perhaps the humorous approach was better. This one, author unknown, at least provided a light touch and some imagination.

It was early in December, as near as I remember,
While walking down the street in tipsy pride,
No one was I disturbing
As I lay down by the curbing,
When a pig came up and lay down by my side.

As I lay there in the gutter, thinking thoughts I cannot utter,
A lady passing by was heard to say,
"You can tell a man who boozes
By the company he chooses,"
And the pig got up and slowly walked away.

A DOLLAR AIN'T A DOLLAR ANY MORE

The high cost of living is another perennial domestic problem. This song was written by Tom Glazer to a tune of unknown origin. Copyright 1947 by People's Songs, Inc. Used by permission of present copyright holder, Sing Out!

Chorus:
Oh, a dollar bill don't buy what it used to,
Don't buy what it used to,
Don't buy what it used to,
Oh, a dollar bill don't buy what it used to,
'Cause a dollar ain't a dollar any more.

Now I live in a rooming house, my room is awful small;
As a matter of fact, it's only two by four;

Then the landlord raised the rent, and now I'm living in the wall
'Cause a dollar ain't a dollar any more.—*Cho.*

From the tree that grows in Brooklyn to the Gulf of Mexico,
From Florida out to the western shore,
Let's grab Congress by the collar, "Roll those prices back," we'll holler,
'Cause a dollar ain't a dollar any more.—*Cho.*

OH, I'M A GOOD OLD REBEL

The solid South and reactionaries anywhere are stoutly represented by this one, written shortly after the War Between the States, and attributed to one of the Randolphs of Virginia.

Oh, I'm a good old rebel,
Now that's just what I am.
For this "Fair land of Freedom"
I do not give a damn.
I'm glad I fit against it,
I only wish we'd won,
And I don't want no pardon
For anything I done.

I followed old Mas' Robert
For four year, near about,
Got wounded in three places
And starved at Pint Lookout;
I cotch the roomatism
A campin' in the snow,
But I killed a chance o' Yankees,
I'd like to kill some mo'.

I hates the Constitution,
This Great Republic, too,
I hates the Freedman's Bureau,
In uniforms of blue;
I hates the nasty eagle,
With all his braggs and fuss,
The lyin', thievin' Yankees,
I hates 'em wuss and wuss.

Three hundred thousand Yankees
Is stiff in southern dust;
We got three hundred thousand
Before they conquered us;
They died of southern fever
And southern steel and shot,
I wish they was three million
Instead of what we got.

I hates the Yankee nation
And everything they do,
I hates the Declaration
Of Independence, too;
I hates the glorious Union—
'Tis dripping with our blood—
I hates their striped banner,
I fit it all I could.

I can't take up my musket
And fight 'em now no more,
But I ain't a-going to love 'em,
Now that is sarten sure;
And I don't want no pardon
For what I was and am,
I won't be reconstructed
And I don't care a damn.

THE OLD GEEZER

Presumably a Union veteran is represented here, since instead of "Old Geezer" another version calls him an old soldier. His philosophy, nowadays, shows a certain kinship with that of his southern opponent.

There was an old geezer and he had a wooden leg;
No tobacco could he borrow, no tobacco could he beg.
Another old geezer was sly as a fox,
And he always had tobacco in his old tobacco box.
Said Geezer Number One, "Will you give me a chew?"
Said Geezer Number Two, "I'll be danged if I do.
You save up your money and you save up your rocks,
And you'll always have tobacco in your old tobacco box."

PITY THE DOWNTRODDEN LANDLORD

From England, this satiric plea, written during World War II by B. Woolf and Arnold Clayton, was caught up by Americans threatened with eviction soon after, and today the song still makes sense in American cities. Copyright by Workers' Music Association, London. Used by permission.

Please open your hearts and your purses
To a man who is misunderstood.
He gets all the kicks and the curses
Though he wishes you nothing but good.
He wistfully begs you to show him
You think he's a friend, not a louse.
So remember the debt that you owe him,
The landlord who lends you his house.

Chorus:
So pity the downtrodden landlord
And his back that is burdened and bent.

Respect his gray hairs, don't ask for repairs,
And don't be behind with the rent.

When a landlord resorts to eviction,
Don't think that he does it for spite;
He is acting from deepest conviction,
And what's right, after all, is what's right.
But I see that your hearts are all hardened,
And I fear I'm appealing in vain;
Yet I hope my last plea will be pardoned,
If I beg on my knees once again:—*Cho.*

THE MAN WHO HAS PLENTY OF GOOD PEANUTS

That what has been called "the good neighbor policy" has been part of American life ever since pioneer days is shown by this old song. Additional verses have been added to include most of the products of a general store or even a mail-order house.

The man who has plenty of good peanuts,
And giveth his neighbor none,
He shan't have any of my peanuts when his peanuts are gone,
When his peanuts are gone, when his peanuts are gone . . .
He shan't have any of my peanuts when his peanuts are gone.

Chorus:
Oh! that will be joyful, joyful, joyful,
Oh; that will be joyful, when his peanuts are gone.

The man who has plenty of nice, rich, ripe, red strawberry shortcake,
And giveth his neighbor none,
He shan't have any of my nice, rich, ripe, red strawberry shortcake,
When his nice, rich, ripe, red strawberry shortcake is gone.—*Cho.*

The man who has plenty of John Wanamaker's endurable, reversible, sit-on-'em
    and mash 'em, patent restorable, operatic plug hats,
And giveth his neighbor none,
He shan't have any of my John Wanamaker's endurable, reversible, sit-on-'em
    and mash 'em, patent restorable, operatic plug hats,
When his John Wanamaker's endurable, reversible, sit-on-'em and mash 'em,
    patent restorable, operatic plug hats are gone.—*Cho.*

The man who has plenty of de-monetized, de-moralized, de-generate, unconsti-
    tutional, saponaceous silver money,
And giveth his neighbor none,
He shan't have any of my de-monetized, de-moralized, de-generate, unconstitu-
    tional, saponaceous silver money,
When his de-monetized, de-moralized, de-generate, unconstitutional, saponaceous
    silver money is gone.—*Cho.*

SHADY ACRES

Those concerned about a "generations gap" should consider that the sympathy for senior citizens expressed in this song was felt by an author-composer who was, at the time, sixteen. Words and music by Janice Ian Fink. Copyright 1967 by Dialogue Music, Inc. Used by permission.

So you've grown tired of your parents hanging around,
They spoil your children and having grandparents is out.
Yes, and they raised you well, but you wish to hell
That they'd go away so you wouldn't have to pay for their food.
Forget all the years when they paid for you.

Chorus:
Send your mother to Shady Acres,
Send your father to Shady Acres,
We'll take good care of them,
You won't be aware of them,
Send them to Shady Acres.

Our home is so peaceful, they die while they're sleeping,
Yes, right in their beds.
Now, there's no need for worry, we have our own mortuary, and a beautiful
    cemetery.
Yes, we are good people, we care for the feeble,
We've devoted our lives to the husbands and wives
Who don't want their fathers around to be bothers.
So send them—we're respectable—and tax deductible.

LITTLE BOXES
(Ticky Tacky)

Crammed with social significance—suburbia, standardization, population explosion—this song by Malvina Reynolds literally did change the author's world when the California town made too famous by her song decided to appoint a planning commission. The compliment of parody was paid by Burt Siegel in the Sing Out! *verses that are included. Original lyric copyright 1962 by Schroder Music Company. All rights reserved. Used by permission.*

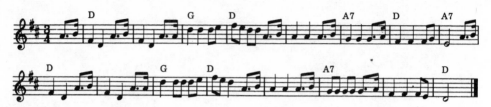

Little boxes on the hillside,
Little boxes made of ticky tacky,
Little boxes on the hillside,
Little boxes all the same.
There's a green one and a pink one
And a blue one and a yellow one,
And they're all made out of ticky tacky
And they all look just the same.

And the people in the houses
All went to the university,
Where they were put in boxes
And they came out all the same.
And there's doctors and there's lawyers,
And business executives,
And they're all made out of ticky tacky
And they all look just the same.

And they all play on the golf course
And drink their martinis dry,
And they all have pretty children
And the children go to school,
And the children go to summer camp
And then to the university,
Where they are put in boxes
And they come out all the same.

And the boys go into business
And marry and raise a family
In boxes made of ticky tacky
And they all look just the same.

Parody:
See, the beatniks in the Village
See, the beatniks on Macdougal Street,
See, the beatniks in the Village,
And they all look just the same.

There's a tall one and a short one,
And a white one and a Negro one.
And they all go to the Village,
And they all look just the same,
And the boys all wear dungarees,
And the girls all wear sandals,
And they're all non-conformists,
And they all dress just the same.

And they go to the university
And they major in philosophy,
And they're all deep thinkers,
And they all think the same,
And they all read their Sartre,
And they all read their Kierkegaard,
And they all talk about it,
But they all sound the same.

And they all like folk music
And they dig Woody Guthrie,
And just like Bob Dylan,
They all sound the same.

HOW'YA GONNA KEEP 'EM DOWN ON THE FARM

Urban growth has gained after every war. This song by Sam M. Lewis and Joe Young, with music by Walter Donaldson, followed World War I in 1919. Copyright © 1919 by Mills Music, Inc. Copyright © renewed 1947 by Mills Music, Inc. Used by permission.

"Reuben, Reuben, I've been thinking,"
Said his wifey dear;
"Now that all is peaceful and calm,
The boys will soon be back on the farm."
Mister Reuben started winking,
And slowly rubbed his chin.
He pulled his chair up close to Mother,
And he asked her with a grin:

Chorus:
"How'ya gonna keep 'em down on the farm,
After they've seen Paree?
How'ya gonna keep 'em away from Broadway,
Jazzin' aroun' an' paintin' the town?
How'ya gonna keep 'em away from harm?
That's a mystery.
They'll never want to see a rake or plow,
And who the deuce can parley-vous a cow?
How'ya gonna keep 'em down on the farm,
After they've seen Paree?"

DAISY BELLE
(A Bicycle Built for Two)

*It wasn't long before the invention of bicycles, which changed things a lot—as the
popular old song by Henry Dacre explains.*

Daisy, Daisy, give me your answer, do!
I'm half crazy, all for the love of you!
It won't be a stylish marriage,

I can't afford a carriage,
But you'll look sweet upon the seat
Of a bicycle built for two.

WAIT FOR THE WAGON

One factor in urban development and rapid change in American life is the speedup of transportation. This old-timer by R. B. Buckley is a reminder of days long past.

Will you come with me, Phyllis dear, to yon blue mountain free?
Where the blossoms smell the sweetest, come rove along with me.
It's every Sunday morning when you are by my side,
We'll jump into the wagon, and we'll all take a ride.

Refrain:
Wait for the wagon, wait for the wagon,
Wait for the wagon and we'll all take a ride.

Where the river runs like silver, and the birds they sing so sweet,
I have a cabin, Phyllis, and something good to eat.
Come listen to my story, it will relieve my heart.
So jump into the wagon, and off we will start.—*Ref.*

WHAT DID YOU LEARN IN SCHOOL TODAY?

Though today's kids learn a lot more than they used to, they don't always learn it in school or aren't "told it like it is." This song by Tom Paxton puts it clearly. Copyright 1963 by Tom Paxton. All rights reserved. Used by permission.

What did you learn in school today,
Dear little boy of mine? *(Repeat.)*

I learned that Washington never told a lie;
I learned that soldiers seldom die;
I learned that everybody's free,

And that's what the teacher said to me,
And that's what I learned in school today,
That's what I learned in school.

What did you learn in school today,
Dear little boy of mine? *(Repeat.)*

I learned our government must be strong,
It's always right and never wrong,
Our leaders are the finest men,
And we elect them again and again,
And that's what I learned in school today,
That's what I learned in school.

What did you learn in school today,
Dear little boy of mine? *(Repeat.)*

I learned that policemen are my friends
I learned that justice never ends,
I learned that murderers die for their crimes,

Even if we make a mistake sometimes,
And that's what I learned in school today,
That's what I learned in school.

What did you learn in school today,
Dear little boy of mine? *(Repeat.)*

I learned that war is not so bad,
I learned of the great ones we had had,
We fought in Germany and in France,
And someday I might get my chance,
And that's what I learned in school today,
That's what I learned in school.

FAIR HARVARD

That the tune is "Believe Me If All Those Endearing Young Charms" and the words painfully antique did not save distinguished alumni, back in the New Deal days, from the charge that Harvard's crimson was really red. Today a verse added on Class Day 1968 brings the old song to date.

Fair Harvard! thy sons to thy jubilee throng,
And with blessings surrender thee o'er,
By these festival rites, from the age that is
past,
To the age that is waiting before.
O relic and type of our ancestor's worth,
That has long kept their memory warm,
First flower of their wilderness! star of their
night,
Calm rising through change and through
storm!

To thy bowers we were led in the bloom of
our youth,
From the home of our infantile years,
When our fathers had warned, and our
mothers had prayed,
And our sisters had blest, through their tears;
Thou then wert our parent, the nurse of our
souls,
We were moulded to manhood by thee,

Till freighted with treasure-thoughts friend-
ships, and hopes,
Thou did'st launch us on Destiny's sea.

Farewell! be thy destinies onward and bright!
To thy children the lesson still give,
With freedom to think, and with patience to
bear,
And for right ever bravely to live.
Let not moss-covered error moor thee at its
side,
As the world on truth's current glides by;
Be the herald of light, and the bearer of love,
Till the stock of the Puritans die.

1968 verse:
The nation that greets us is tortured and sick
And mouths inarticulate cures.
We pray for the spirit to cope with a world
Where so very little assures.

THE EYES OF TEXAS

Claims for the Texas University song, its tune derived from an old hymn, have as a basis not only the fact that for some years anyone humming the tune in a Washington elevator acquired a chorus; it also had a definite political effect when, in 1917, students sang it under the windows of a governor about to be impeached. So he was—an early example of effective political protest in song.

The eyes of Texas are upon you,
All the livelong day.
The eyes of Texas are upon you,
You cannot get away.

Do not think you can escape them
At night or early in the morn—
The eyes of Texas are upon you
Till Gabriel blows his horn.

COYOTE, MY LITTLE BROTHER

In the machine age, wildlife suffers most; and although a bounty was once offered for his hide, Peter La Farge had a sympathetic word for the coyote now vanishing from the Southwest. Copyright 1968 by Peter La Farge; published in Broadside as transcribed by Sis Cunningham. Used by permission.

Coyot', Coyotee-ee-ee! What have they done?
My little brother, where . . . where do you run?
Little Brother, where . . . where do you run?
They strychnined the mountains, they strychnined the plains
My little brother, the coyote, won't come back again.

When you hear him singing, the few that are left,
He's warning the human race of his death.

Don't poison the mesas, don't poison the sky,
Or you won't be back; little brother, goodbye.

There will be no one to listen, and no one to sing,
And never and never will there be spring.

Coyot', Coyotee-ee-ee! What have they done?

WAIST DEEP IN THE BIG MUDDY

For those who want to say it out loud there's television, but not always. This is the song TV censors cut from a proposed broadcast by Pete Seeger. Though based on an incident in a boot camp down South, the lyric was considered a criticism of American foreign policy. Copyright 1966 by Ludlow Music. All rights reserved. Used by permission.

It was back in nineteen forty-two,
I was part of a good platoon.
We were on maneuvers in-a Looziana,
One night by the light of the moon.
The captain told us to ford a river,
And that's how it all begun.
We were knee deep in the Big Muddy,
But the damn fool said to push on.

The sergeant said, Sir, are you sure
This is the best way back to the base?
Sergeant, go on; I've forded this river
Just a mile above this place.
It'll be a little soggy but just keep slogging,
We'll soon be on dry ground.
We were waist deep in the Big Muddy,
And the damn fool said to push on.

The sergeant said, With all this equipment
No man'll be able to swim.
Sergeant, don't be a nervous Nellie,
The captain said to him;
All we need is a little determination.
Men, follow me, I'll lead on.
We were neck deep in the Big Muddy,
And the damn fool said to push on.

All of a sudden, the moon clouded over,
We heard a gurgling cry.
A few seconds later, the captain's helmet
Was all that floated by.
The sergeant said, Turn around, men,
I'm in charge from now on,
And we just made it out of the Big Muddy,
With the captain dead and gone.

Next day from a boat we found his body
Stuck in the old quicksand.
I guess he didn't know that the water was
    deeper
Than the place he'd once before been.
Another stream had joined the Big Muddy
Just a half mile from where we'd gone.
We'd been lucky to escape from the Big
    Muddy
When the damn fool said to push on.

Well, maybe you'd rather not draw any moral,
I'll leave that to yourself.
Maybe you're still walking and you're still
    talking
And you'd like to keep your health.
But every time I read the papers
That old feeling comes on,
Waist deep in the Big Muddy
And the Big Fool says to push on.

Waist deep in the Big Muddy,
And the Big Fool says to push on
Waist deep in the Big Muddy
And the Big Fool says to push on
[Whistle a cadenza for two lines]
Waist deep in the BIG MUDDY!
AND THE BIG FOOL SAYS TO PUSH ON!

I READ IT IN THE DAILY NEWS

Even when forests are pulped into newsprint, it's hard to keep up with all that goes on in the world today. This song, with words and music by Tom Paxton, discusses that problem. © Copyright 1964 by Deep Fork Music, Inc. All rights reserved. Used by permission.

Civil-rights leaders are a pain in the neck,
Can't hold a candle to Chiang Kai-shek.
Ban-the-bombers are afraid of a fight,
Peace hurts business and that ain't right.
How do I know? I read it in the *Daily News.*

Chorus:
Daily News, daily blues,
Pick up a copy any time you choose.
Seven little pennies in the newsboy's hand,
And you ride right along to never-never land.

We've got to bomb Castro, bomb him flat.
He's too damn successful and we can't risk
    that.
How do I know? I read it in the *Daily News.*
There's millions of commies in the freedom
    fight,
Yellin' for Lenin and civil rights.
How do I know? I read it in the *Daily News.*
    —Cho.

It seems like the whole damn world's gone
    wrong,
Saint Joe McCarthy is dead and gone.
How do I know? I read it in the *Daily News*
Don't try to change my mind with facts,
To hell with the graduated income tax.
How do I know? I read it in the *Daily News*
    —Cho

You know, John Paul Getty is just plain folks
The UN charter is a cruel hoax.
How do I know? I read it in the *Daily News*
J. Edgar Hoover is the Man of the Hour,
All that he needs is just a little more power.
How do I know? I read it in the *Daily News*
    —Cho

WOODMAN, SPARE THAT TREE

Concern about the waste of wood pulp and for the vanishing redwoods had its counterpart in a more personal and sentimental age. These verses by George Pope Morris, set to a tune by Henry Russell, were recited as well as sung.

Woodman, spare that tree! Touch not a single bough!
In youth it sheltered me, and I'll protect it now.
'Twas my forefather's hand that placed it near his cot—
There, woodman, let it stand, thy axe shall harm it not!

That old familiar tree, its glory and renown
Are spread o'er land and sea, and wouldst thou hew it down?
Woodman, forbear thy stroke! Cut not its earthbound ties.
Oh, spare that aged oak now tow'ring to the skies.

My heartstrings round thee cling, close as thy bark, old friend.
Here shall the wild birds sing, and still thy branches bend.
Old tree, the storm thou'lt brave, and, woodman, leave the spot.
While I've a hand to save, thy axe shall harm it not.

MY DIRTY STREAM

Pete Seeger deplores pollution of the Hudson as it flows past Bear Mountain and Manhattan Island. Copyright 1964 by Fall River Music. All rights reserved. Used by permission.

Sailing down this dirty stream,
Still I love it and I'll keep the dream
That someday, though maybe not this year,
My Hudson River will once again run clear.
It starts high in the mountains of the North,
Crystal clear and icy, trickles forth,
With just a few wrappers of chewing gum
Dropped by hikers to warn of things to come.

At Glens Falls 5,000 honest hands
Work at the consolidated paper plant;
Five million gallons of waste a day,
Why should we do it any other way?
Down the valley one million toilet chains

Find my Hudson so convenient place to drain
Each little city says, "Who me?"
Do you think that sewage plants come free?

In the great ocean they say the water's clear,
But I live right at Beacon here.
Halfway between the mountains and the sea,
Tacking to and fro, this thought occurs to me,
Sailing up my dirty stream:
Still I love it and I'll dream
That someday, though maybe not this year,
Yes, my Hudson and my country will run
    clear.

I'M GONNA SAY IT NOW

Phil Ochs, always an articulate spokesman for his generation, here speaks and sings for them. Copyright 1965 by Barricade Music, Inc., Tipanga, California. All rights reserved. Used by permission.

Oh, I am just a student, sir,
And I only want to learn.
But it's hard to read through the risin' smoke
Of the books that you like to burn.
So I'd like to make a promise,
And I'd like to make a vow,
That when I've got somethin' to say, sir,
I'm gonna say it now.

I've read of other countries where
The students take a stand;
They've even helped to overthrow
The leaders of the land.
Now I wouldn't go so far to say
We're also learnin' how,
But when, etc. . . .

There's a time you gotta study
And a time you gotta fight
And a time to go to college
And learn about your rights,
And you can learn it fast or slow
But learn it anyhow
That when I've got, etc. . . .

XIII

SONGS FOR A MOVING WORLD

"Yes, but it does move," Galileo is said to have murmured sotto voce even as he was forced to recant his discovery of the world's motion. That the world does indeed move and that the motion is on the whole safe, and even beneficial to earth dwellers, is now generally believed; and the happier people believe also that they can see a trend in human affairs that is, on the whole, forward.

Today's protest songs, along with the prophets of all the ages, try to outline paths of progress and to reassure those alarmed by movement. Perhaps most reassuring is that, as this book has tried to show, the patient and hopeful songs even of the days of slavery pledge a faith in the future that makes them helpful still, while today's new songs are concerned and full of proposals for improvement. And songs, as such, can help. In the words of John Brunner, the British writer of lyrics for today, "There's all the difference in the world between trudging through the rain with squelching shoes and your head miserably bowed, and trudging through the rain singing at the top of your voice." *

* Quoted in *Broadside,* February, 1963, referring to the Aldermaston peace march.

OL' ARK'S A-MOVERIN'

First among world stories suggesting safety in motion, the ark that Noah built is the historic answer to standpatters. Also, of course, this spiritual may have told Negroes that it was safer to move up north.

Chorus:
Oh, de ol' ark's a-moverin', a-moverin',
    a-moverin',
De ol' ark's a-movin', by de spirit o' God!
Oh, de ol' ark's a-moverin', a-moverin',
    a-moverin',
De ol' ark's a-movin' an' I thank God.

How many days did the water fall?
Forty days an' nights in all.
Ol' ark she reel, ol' ark, she rock,
Ol' ark she landed on the mountaintop.—*Cho.*

Ham, Shem, and Japheth was a-settin' one day,
Talkin' on de upper deck an' lookin' down
    de bay,
An' while dey was a-sputin' 'bout dis an' dat,
De ark done bump on Ararat.—*Cho.*

EZEKIEL SAW DE WHEEL

Ezekiel saw another phase of progress: The spiritual that interprets the prophet makes clear that as the wheels go round and round, the world goes on.

Chorus:
Ezekiel saw de wheel, 'way up in de middle ob de air,
Ezekiel saw de wheel, 'way in the middle ob de air;
And de little wheel run by faith, and de big wheel run by de grace ob God,
'Tis a wheel in a wheel, 'way in de middle ob de air.

Some go to church fo' to sing and shout, 'way in de middle ob de air,
Befo' six months dey are all turned out, 'way in de middle ob de air.—*Cho.*

Let me tell you what a hypocrite'll do, 'way in de middle ob de air,
He'll talk 'bout me and he'll talk 'bout you, 'way in de middle ob de air.
—*Cho.*

One ob dese days about twelve o'clock, 'way in de middle ob de air,
An' dis ol' world gwine to reel and rock, 'way in de middle ob de air.—*Cho.*

THIS OLD WORLD IS CHANGING HANDS

One phase of progress by turnover is observed by Phil Ochs in a lyric that might well be illustrated by maps or a radar screen. Copyright 1964 by Appleseed Music, Inc., New York, N.Y. All rights reserved. Used by permission.

Oh, a thousand marching armies and a million marching men
Have won the wide world over and lost it back again.
But now the word has gone to every fallen land
That this old world is changin' hands.

Chorus:
From the master to the servant, from the owner to the slave,
Colonial days are buried in a deep and dirty grave.
It's so easy to see, and well to understand,
That this old world is changin' hands.

Washington and Jefferson and Patrick Henry, too,
They knew what they were doin' when they started somethin' new;
It was in this giant land of ours that it all began
When this old world was changin' hands.—*Cho.*

And when World War II was rollin' by the tide was on its way,
Many countries had to listen to the words they had to say;
And the sign was seen by millions all of yellow, black and tan,
That this old world is changin' hands.—*Cho.*

GOD'S GOIN' TO SET THIS WORLD ON FIRE

This spiritual, according to Carl Sandburg, spread from Negro churches to IWW gatherings back in the thirties. It had nothing to do with Hiroshima or napalm.

God's goin' to set this world on fire,
God's goin' to set this world on fire,
One o' these days!
God's goin' to set this world on fire,
One o' these days!

We are climbin' Jacob's ladder,
We are climbin' Jacob's ladder,
Some o' these days.
Every round goes higher and higher,
Some o' these days.

WE'RE GONNA MOVE

This marching song from SNCC is reassuring rather than alarming to those who, with its singers, have faith in spiritual guidance. Copyright 1965 by SNCC. All rights reserved. Used by permission.

We're gonna move when the spirit say "move,"
We're gonna move when the spirit say "move,"
'Cause when the spirit say "move," why then
    you move with the spirit.
Got to move when the spirit say move.

You've got to march when the spirit say march, etc.

You've got to sing, etc.

You've got to cool it, etc.

You've got to jump, etc.

You've got to pray, etc.

HOW LONG

The question "How long, O Lord, how long?" has echoed down the ages, and this song by Phil Ochs offers one answer in the line "There is no future in the past." Copyright 1963 by Phil Ochs. First published in Broadside.

How long, how long can we go on—
How long, how long can we go on?
This troubled land may never last;
There is no future in the past.

Chorus:
Why the fear of the comin' of the mornin',
Why the tremblin' at the call?

Can't we hear the final warnin',
Can't we see the writin' on the wall?

How far, how far have we gone—
How far, how far have we gone?
So many battles without a gain,
So many young men lost in vain.—*Cho.*

HE'S GOT THE WHOLE WORLD IN HIS HANDS

Marian Anderson, many will remember, sang this one on the steps of the Lincoln Memorial after the DAR declined to let her sing in Constitution Hall. The parody by Sam Cooke that follows Miss Anderson's version was adapted for singing by protest marchers in Chicago long before the Democratic convention of 1968.

He's got the whole world in His hands,
He's got the whole world in His hands,
He's got the whole world in His hands,
He's got the whole world in His hands.

He's got the little babies in His hands,
He's got the little babies in His hands,
He's got the little babies in His hands,
He's got the whole world in His hands.

He's got the gamblin' man in His hands,
He's got the gamblin' man in His hands,
He's got the gamblin' man in His hands,
He's got the whole world in His hands.

He's got you and me, brother, in His hands,
He's got you and me, sister, in His hands,
He's got you and me, brother, in His hands,
He's got the whole world in His hands.

He's got the whole world in His hands,
He's got the whole world in His hands,
He's got the whole world in His hands,
He's got the whole world in His hands.

Parody:
We got the whole world shakin' now
                              (Repeat 3 times.)
Something must be goin' on.

We got to keep on pushin' now *(Repeat.)*
Just a little way to go.

We got the whole city brimmin' now *(Repeat.)*
Got a movement goin' on.

We got the whole world shakin' now *(Repeat.)*
Dr. King is on his way.
We got to keep on pushin' now
And we might get Freedom today.

THE UNITED NATIONS

Those who regard the United Nations as the world's last, best hope may find encouragement for the life of that organization and of the world in this song with music by Shostakovich and words by Harold Rome. From the songbook of Highlander Folk School, Monteagle, Tennessee.

The sun and the stars all are ringing,
With song rising from the earth.
The hope of humanity singing
A hymn to a new world in birth.

Refrain:
United Nations on the march with
    flags unfurl'd,
Together fight for victory, a Free New World.
                        (Repeat.)

Take heart all you nations swept under,
By powers of darkness that ride,
The wrath of the people shall thunder,
Relentless as time and the tide.—*Ref.*

As sure as the sun meets the morning,
And rivers go down to the sea,
A new day for mankind is dawning,
Our children shall live proud and free!—*Ref.*

Refrain:
United Nations on the march with
    flags unfurl'd,
Together fight for victory, a Free New World.

THERE ARE STRANGE THINGS HAPPENING

Printed as a broadside by Negro preachers in East Texas during World War I, this song is attributed to John Handcox who also wrote, to the same tune, "There Is Mean Things Happening in This Land."

There are strange things happening in this land,
There are strange things happening in this land;
For the war is going on, causing many hearts to mourn,
There are strange things happening in this land.

You read also of famines that are coming in the land,
And if you notice closely you can better understand,
For provisions are so high, it is hard for you to buy,
There are strange things happening in this land.

Nations up against nations are rising in the land,
Kingdoms against kingdoms, you see and understand;
And there's no need to cry for the end is drawing nigh.
There are strange things happening in this land.

The word of God is true, and we know that it is right,
Before the end of time many nations will fight.
There are thousands lying dead from the blood they have shed,
There are strange things happening in this land.

The kaiser is fighting and making every charge,
And trying to win the victory that his land might be enlarged.
He is fighting everywhere, land and sea and in the air,
There are strange things happening in this land.

They tried to fool the Negroes, saying they ought not to fight,
They have no home, no country, no flag, no civil rights.
But the Negroes knew best, and their deeds will prove the rest.
There are strange things happening in this land.

When Uncle Sammie called them, they answered, "Here are we
To do a soldier's duty wherever it may be."
They answered true and brave, in the trenches made their grave.
There are strange things happening in this land.

Come, let's respect Old Glory and hold the banner high.
It's not for territory that we are willing to die,
But it's for human rights we have entered in this fight.
There are strange things happening in this land.

God declared his judgment against every nation wrong,
On rulers from the president to the kaiser on his throne.
And the kaiser knows well when he dies he is going to hell.
There are strange things happening in this land.

Go tell old Billie Kaiser that Woodrow Wilson said
He will never quit fighting until he kills him dead.
There he will ring the Liberty Bell, give old kaiser room in hell,
There are great things happening in this land.

MY LORD, WHAT A MOURNING

This is the spiritual played over and over on the air when commercials were cut off for more important communications, on the day FDR died.

My Lord, what a mourning,
My Lord, what a mourning,
My Lord, what a mourning
When the stars begin to fall.

You'll hear the trumpet sound
To wake the nations underground
Looking to my God's right hand,
When the stars begin to fall.

INDEX OF SONG TITLES

INDEX OF FIRST LINES

Y